HUNTERS
OF THE
WILD

Michael Bright

HUNTING ANIMALS AND
THEIR STRATEGIES

HUNTERS
OF THE
WILD

Michael Bright

HUNTING ANIMALS AND
THEIR STRATEGIES

PRION

First published in the United Kingdom 1992 by Prion,
an imprint of Multimedia Books Ltd, London.

Published in the United States 1993 by Prion

Editor: Linda Osband
Design: Megra Mitchell
Picture Research: Charlotte Deane
Production: Hugh Allan

Typeset by Megra Mitchell
Printed in Hong Kong by Imago

ISBN 1-85375-088-3

Contents

Ambush

1

Predators are an important element in the web of life. They do not kill and consume all the prey. A balance exists between predators trying to catch prey and prey animals trying to outwit predators. It is an evolutionary arms race, in which neither wins. As soon as a predator has the advantage, the prey develops effective anti-predator behaviour and the strong and healthy survive. The hunters keep populations healthy by weeding out the old and the sick.

Many predators prefer a quick kill. It is a matter of self-preservation. A predator cannot afford to allow the prey to thrash about. Flailing hooves or dangerous claws may inflict an injury, followed by infection, that puts the predator out of action. Civets bite into the back of the head, throwing themselves on to their back or side, and use their feet to push away the prey's feet and claws. Cats bite into the neck, their large canines prising apart the neck bones of small prey items, the hold constricting the windpipe of larger victims. Dogs and sharks enhance the action of their teeth with a violent shaking of the head.

But whatever the means of dispatching the prey, the predator must first find and catch its food. It must go hunting, and one of the favourite strategies for predators hunting alone is to take prey by surprise – the ambush.

TIGER, TIGER

A CHITAL DEER stag grazes in a forest clearing in a national park in India. Approaching in the undergrowth behind, downwind of the deer, a Bengal tiger presses itself close to the ground. The tiger is camouflaged well, its stripes blending in with the background of dappled light and shadows in the foliage. It has searched for 10 miles or more before spotting a suitable target, one in which there is sufficient cover to hide the predator's stealthy approach.

Slowly, the tiger moves closer, lying still each time the stag looks up. It stalks with body flattened and head erect. The hunter must be within 60ft of its prey before it can launch a suitable attack. Any further away and the stag will bolt, its superior speed making good its escape. As the moment of attack approaches, the

The tiger is the largest living cat. These young Bengal tigers, living on the Indian sub-continent, may grow up to 10ft (3m) long (including 3ft (1m) of tail), while the even larger Siberian tigers of Siberia and Manchuria are reputed to grow to 13ft (4m) long. Tigers mainly hunt alone, but mothers usually hunt with their offspring until they are old enough to fend for themselves.

HUNTERS AND HUNTED

Predators kill other animals. They eat meat. More than often they kill plant eaters. Herbivores must process vast quantities of plant food in order to obtain their daily needs, but having done so they concentrate the nutrients in their bodies and they become the targets for hunters. Predators spend their time and energy finding and catching the highly nutritious plant eaters and, therefore, need eat less often and consume smaller quantities of food. Predators, surprisingly, have a poor time in catching prey. They are not as efficient hunters as one might imagine. Wildlife films on television often show the cream of the hunts, but success is infrequent. A leopard, hunting alone in East Africa, succeeds in running down an antelope or a gazelle in about one in twenty attacks. Groups do better. A third of spotted hyena attacks end in a successful kill, and wild dogs succeed half the time.

tiger rocks back on its limbs and gathers itself up, every muscle straining for the rapid release.

Suddenly it charges and, in a few strides, slams into the prey. The stag is large and does not fall, but a slap from the huge forepaw trips the deer and the tiger grabs it by the back of the neck. With its hind limbs remaining on the ground, the big cat bites into the deer's throat and the two go crashing to the ground. The tiger hangs on, the bite crushing the windpipe. The deer suffocates, but the predator does not let go until it is convinced that the deer is dead.

The carcass is dragged away and into the cover of bushes, where the feast can begin. Over 70lb of meat might be eaten at one sitting, the rest devoured over several days. Tigers tend to stay with their kills until every morsel is consumed. Each year, a solitary hunter will make 40-60 similar kills, feeding on average once a week.

Most cats hunt alone and must rely on stealth to catch a meal. The tiger is the biggest and most powerful, and is such a well-adapted killer that it can take on prey larger than itself and win, although nine out of ten attacks may be unsuccessful.

The tiger is a typical cat, with large eyes giving binocular, colour vision. During the day cats' eyes are about the same as ours, but in the night they are six times better. They also have good hearing, but a less well-developed sense of smell than dogs. The forepaws have long, very sharp, scimitar-like retractile claws that can grab and hold on to prey. The jaws have strong muscles and large canine teeth that give the tiger a powerful killing bite. At the kill, the tiger sometimes grabs its prey well forward, pressing the head to the ground and using its forepaw as a lever to topple the victim over. The prey falls awkwardly and breaks its own neck.

Although more usually a solitary predator, a tiger mother and her cubs might hunt co-operatively. With more mouths to feed, the tiger family will kill up to 70 deer or other animals, such as wild pigs and gaurs, a year.

SPOTTED PROWLERS

WHERE THE TIGER has stripes, the leopard has spots, another equally effective form of cryptic (hidden) coloration. And like the tiger, the leopard uses stealth to track and catch prey. Hunting is usually carried out at night, the prey spotted from a vantage-point, such as a tree or rocky outcrop. The leopard stalks or ambushes, depending on local conditions. It rarely pounces on prey directly from a tree. It jumps down before launching an attack, rushing a victim before it has time to escape.

Being smaller than the other big cats and hunting alone, the leopard is vulnerable to thieving lions and hyenas. It drags its prize, sometimes the large carcass of an antelope, to a stand of trees and hauls it up into a fork, where it can feed in comparative safety.

The South American jaguar is larger than the leopard but resembles it closely. It lives in forests, where it stalks or ambushes monkeys in the trees, deer and peccaries on the ground, and fish in the rivers. It is rumoured to wriggle its tail in the water to attract fish, but this behaviour has yet to be confirmed by scientific observation.

Snow leopards, living in the mountains of southern Asia, have few things to catch. Animals are widely scattered, so these mountain hunters must follow the vertical seasonal migration of wild sheep and goats in order to track a meal. In

The leopard is a secretive and solitary predator, mainly active after dark. It spends much of the day lying in deep cover, in caves or amongst rocks, stirring in late afternoon to go hunting in the evening and during the night.

snow, the snow leopard has the advantage. The soles of its feet are lined with a cushion of thick hair, which enables the cat to run over soft snow without it sinking in.

SMALL CATS

THE SMALLER MEMBERS of the cat family ambush their prey in one of two ways: some patrol their home range and approach prey stealthily, while others wait for the prey to come to them.

If snow-shoe hares are abundant, the Canadian lynx lies on a 'hunting bed' and pounces on passing animals. When scarce, it must travel many miles in search of a single hare, and then creep up quietly to surprise it. It is more successful chasing over hard snow than over new-lain snow. In soft snow, lighter animals are able to outrun the lynx and get away.

The serval of Africa differs from most other cats in relying on hearing rather than sight to detect small mammals. It has large, widely spaced ears with which it can pick up the slightest movement. Once located, the serval pounces, leaping into the air and landing on the victim with its forepaws. The prey, if not already dead, is killed with a bite to the nape of the neck. Servals can also pick up the shuffling of mole rats underground and they have two ways in which they catch them. Those in shallow burrows are simply dug out, but those in deeper burrows present more of a problem. It is solved when the serval damages the entrance to the tunnel and simply waits patiently for the occupant to appear to repair it. As soon as its head appears, the serval strikes.

Caracals and ocelot sometimes ambush birds. Stalking does not work, for the birds tend to flap away. The cats must rush the target and pin it down with the front paws and claws. Margays and clouded leopards wait in trees and pounce on their prey as it passes below.

Fishing cats do not hook fish out with the paw like domestic tabbies. Instead, the fishing cat places its face close to the water surface, peers into the gloom and then pushes its head below to grab a fish in its mouth.

ARCTIC LONER

THE POLAR BEAR is the largest of the land-living carnivores, and one of the most powerful predators in the Arctic. It is at home on land and in the sea, a layer of fat and thick fur keeping it warm in its frozen world.

The serval is a long-legged small cat that also hunts mainly at night. It follows well-worn paths across the savannah and catches guinea fowl, hares and small rodents such as cane rats.

Polar bears are nomadic, preferring to travel to and from regular sites where food is seasonally plentiful. In early spring, bears seek out the breeding dens of ringed seals, which are found buried below the snow over sea ice. Using brute force the bear crashes through the roof of the den, surprising the seal family and grabbing the youngsters.

Adult seals are caught when they come up to breathe. The bears sit patiently next to the breathing holes, identified by the oily secretions on the surrounding ice, and wait until the seal's head appears. Quick as lightning, the bear's enormous forepaw strikes out and hooks the seal up on to the ice, its skull crushed with one bludgeon-like blow to the head or its neck broken with one bite of the polar bear's formidable jaws.

Seals and their pups hauled out on ice flows are stalked from across the ice and in the water. The bear uses ridges and dips to conceal its approach, slipping into the water for the final few yards. It paddles gently forward, resembling a chunk of floating ice, and then rushes the victim in a swirl of water.

One polar bear was once seen to stalk a seal and each time the victim turned, the bear would freeze and place its paw over its black nose to prevent the seal from spotting it. Ringed seals are the most common seals in the Arctic and so constitute the bulk of the polar bear diet, although bearded, hooded and harp seals are sometimes taken. At Wrangel Island in the East Siberia Sea, polar bears attack walruses and their pups. Over-enthusiastic bears jump on the backs of the adults, but are dislodged by one shake of the walrus's enormous bulk. The thick layer of blubber protects them from the polar bear's teeth and claws. The bears are only successful if they can ambush a young walrus before it escapes to the sea.

KILLER SEALS

AT THE OTHER end of the world lives another master of ambush, the leopard seal. Leopard seals - 10ft long, with large, reptile-like heads and huge jaws studded with vicious teeth - are also solitary hunters. They catch just about anything that moves in the Southern Ocean, as long as it is smaller and more vulnerable, but their favourite food is penguins. The ambush often takes place at the edge of an ice shelf near a penguin colony, at places where penguins dive into the water to go fishing. If a leopard seal is about, penguins are noticeably agitated and are reluctant to leave the safety of the ice. Eventually, weight of numbers forces the first birds to take the plunge; just what the seal has been waiting for.

The penguin is grabbed in the jaws, violently shaken and swallowed whole, minus the head and feet. Large birds, like emperor and king penguins, are dealt with in a different fashion; they are shaken until the skin splits and then 'unwrapped'. A powerful flick of the seal's head literally peels off the bird's skin and feathers as far as the chin and legs, and the large breast muscles are consumed, leaving the rest.

AMBUSH FROM THE AIR

EAGLES, HAWKS and falcons ambush from the air. The harpy eagle, which haunts the jungles of South America, can spot movement through the foliage of the jungle canopy, swoop down, fly momentarily upside down and snatch a sloth hanging beneath a branch.

The osprey hunts over water and catches fish. It patrols a stretch of coast or lakeside, watching for fish just below the surface. Then, it plunges into the

Out of water, the leopard seal is a clumsy sea mammal which penguins ignore. In the sea, it is a super-efficient killer, well able to out-manoeuvre and catch fast-swimming prey. Its head has been likened to that of a reptile rather than a mammal.

water, the feet thrust forward just before impact, and the fish is grabbed in the talons. The feet are strong to take the force of the hit, and the claws long and sharp to anchor the prey. Rough spicules on the undersides of the toes help grip the slippery fish. The grip is so tight that birds have been known to be dragged below the surface by particularly large fish.

Having made a catch, the osprey slowly flaps its way back into the sky, the wriggling fish hanging below. Once airborne, the fish is held with the head facing forwards to reduce air resistance. It is taken back to the nest or a favourite eating perch.

Fish eagles and sea eagles do not plunge into the water, but snatch fish from the surface. They have longer, less stocky legs than the osprey and do not confine themselves to eating fish. Hares and seal pups fall prey to sea eagles. And in East Africa, one soda lake devoid of fish has its fish eagles taking young flamingoes instead of more orthodox prey.

Crowned eagles and martial eagles grab monkeys from treetops, or knock them out of the branches so that they are killed on the ground. These birds can take mammals many times their own weight - African hawk eagles catch hares four times their size and tawny eagles grab small antelope called dik-dik, which weigh 8lb or more.

The kestrel, the buzzard and European snake eagle hover before making a snatch. By hovering, the bird has an aerial perch from which it can scan the ground below. The wings and long tail of the kestrel are fanned out, and air currents are used to keep the bird in one place. The head remains rock steady.

Large eagles, particularly those living in mountainous regions, have wings adapted for soaring flight. The wings are broad, with 6 or 7 loose primaries at the wing tip. These are movable and act as 'slots' to help in flight control. While soaring along the slope of a mountain, a bird is buffeted by air currents, but by adjusting these feathers, the eagle maintains a level flight, an obvious aid to hunting.

GIGANTIC SMILING JAWS

NILE CROCODILES ARE big, growing to 20ft long, and their tastes are catholic. They take anything from hippopotamus calves to ducks, and zebras to frogs, but by far the most common prey are fish, which represent about 70 per cent of their diet. The fish are pursued through the water, caught in the jaws and slammed continuously against a rock until dead. They are then manoeuvred into the mouth head first and swallowed.

Larger animals are ambushed at the water's edge. Antelope, zebras and even young lions and elephants fall prey to crocodiles. The giant reptiles slide slowly into the water and glide gently towards the river-bank, only the nostrils and eyes showing above the water. When a victim is spotted, the crocodile sinks without leaving a ripple and swims unseen below the surface. As the thirsty animal bends down to take a drink, the crocodile grabs it by the snout, toppling it over into the water. Using its superior power and weight, it is able to pull the prey down and drown it. The carcass is dismembered by grasping a limb or wedge of flesh in the mouth and revolving the entire body until the chunk of meat is torn away.

Carrion can provide crocodiles with sudden gluts of food. During the great wildebeest migration in East Africa, millions of animals must cross the Mara River each September. Waiting for them on the river-banks are the

A martial eagle, one of the largest of Africa's eagles, has caught a squirrel in its powerful talons. Although mainly a hunter of gamebirds, large martial eagles may take vervet monkeys and even dik-diks.

predators - lions, leopards, wild dogs, hyenas - and, in the water, crocodiles lurk below the surface. Stragglers and poor swimmers are grabbed from below. They are dragged against the current, the only visible sign that they have been attacked. Many animals simply drown, failing to reach the far bank or clamber from the water. For the crocodiles it is a food bonanza.

Stalking large mammals, such as hippos and elephants, can be hazardous. Elephants trample crocodiles underfoot and hippos have been known to bite a large specimen in two. In the Tana River in Kenya, a 6ft-long Nile crocodile took on a 15ft python and, after a 2-hour battle, it lost. The python crushed the crocodile to death and swallowed it whole. A crocodile in St Lucia came to an untimely end when a large terrapin became lodged in its throat. But perhaps the most bizarre story involved a young crocodile that attacked a giraffe in the Kruger National Park, South Africa. The crocodile grabbed its victim by the snout, in the usual crocodile fashion, but the giraffe just raised its head, hoisting the startled reptile high into the air. Eventually, the crocodile let go, dropping back into the river, and the giraffe, bruised but not badly injured, sauntered off.

Nile crocodiles are man-eaters. At one time it was estimated that these killers accounted for over 3,000 deaths a year. Today, with reduced crocodile popula-

A Nile crocodile launches a surprise attack on exhausted wildebeest. The crocodiles lie almost invisible below the surface of the Mara River in Kenya, ready to ambush their prey. The wildebeest must cross the river on the annual migration and many drown or are taken by the waiting predators.

tions throughout Africa, the deaths are fewer; but they still occur, most often bathers or women taking their washing to the river. In 1987, a young Coldstream Guards officer rescued a South African boy from the Zambezi. Together with the boy's father (who lost an arm in the rescue, and a British student, the army officer (who had his arms broken) wrenched the boy from the crocodile's jaws. He received the British Humane Society's silver medal.

SHADOWS IN THE SEA

IN THE SEA, the great white shark is responsible for the most shark attacks on people. It is a giant amongst sharks, reaching 25ft in length, and the only predictable thing about it is its unpredictability.

The great white is found in all the world's oceans, in temperate as well as tropical waters. Young sharks tend to eat mainly fish and squid, but when they get to a certain size - about 13ft long - they take to eating warm-blooded prey, mainly sea mammals such as seals, sea-lions and sea-otters.

Off the coast of California, great whites take elephant seals.

In the autumn, bull elephant seals begin to arrive at breeding beaches along the California coast. One of these colonies is on the Farallon Islands, due west of San Francisco. When they arrive at the beach, the bulls must fight for the right to mate and so tend to wait offshore, sizing up the opposition. Their reluctance to go ashore can be fatal.

Below them, a shadow silently slices through the water, manoeuvring itself into position so that its grey-coloured back blends in with the dark background of rocks rather than the lighter-coloured sand. On the islands, western gulls rise as one into the air. They have spotted the almost imperceptible movements below the surface and anticipate feeding time. They have seen the signs before and know what is about to take place.

Rising below and behind a seal, the shadow that is an enormous great white accelerates. The snout lifts and the jaws protrude forward in an eerie grimace, which reveals rows of triangular, slicing, saw-like teeth. The eyes swivel back into their protective sockets. Swimming blind, only guided by sensors in the snout that detect the muscle activity of the prey, the shark prepares for the impact. But at the last moment, the seal spots the movement below and jigs to one side. The shark, unable to stop, surges out of the water, most of its body clearing the surface. It drops back in with an enormous splash and disappears into the depths from whence it came.

Nearby, another shark slams into the side of a less fortunate young bull seal, and, in a flurry of blood and foam, it takes a huge chunk of blubber and flesh. The attack is brief and debilitating. The shark stands off, waiting for the seal to bleed to death before it begins to feed. The claws of a full-grown elephant seal could do great damage to a shark and so it adopts a 'bite-and-wait' policy. The gulls gather round, feeding on pieces of the victim's skin and flesh.

When finally the seal succumbs, the shark must eat as much as it can take. A 70lb chunk of blubber will provide enough nutrients to keep it going for a month and a half, and it may have to exist for many months before it obtains another meal. A great white's stomach temperature is raised about 6 degrees C directly after feeding, an adaptation that speeds up digestion so that the shark is ready to feed again.

Great whites repeat this pattern of attack at seal and sea-lion colonies along the Pacific coast of North America, a stretch of shoreline noted not only for its wildlife, but also for its surfers and bathers. Here, nature comes into conflict with the recreational needs of people. Modern surfboards, complete with dangling arms and legs, resemble seals from below. And what is more, these 'seals' behave strangely, drawing the attention of predators just as old and sick animals do on the African plains. The result is inevitable. Surfers near seal colonies are attacked and some are killed.

The shark follows its normal attack pattern, coming from below and behind, but, by the time it has realised its mistake and the expectation of a juicy seal steak turns into the reality of a wooden surfboard, it is too late. The shark slams into its target and, programmed by its 'bite-and-wait' type of predatory behaviour that has taken millions of years of evolution to perfect, it waits nearby for the surfboard to 'die'. It is this stand-off behaviour that has allowed many people to survive an attack from what is the largest and most powerful predatory fish in the sea. If they are not badly injured and have not lost too much blood, there is the slender chance of them staying alive.

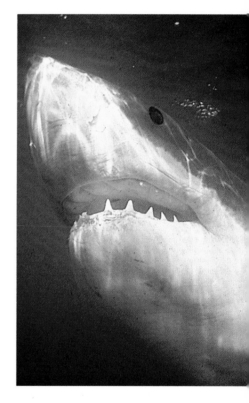

The great white shark is the largest fish in the world and one of the sea's supreme predators. Its jaws are filled with row upon row of serrated, triangular teeth capable of slicing through flesh, blubber and bone. It takes single, large bites, the lower teeth, just visible in the photograph, holding the prey and the upper ones, aided by a sideways shaking of the head, shearing away a mouthful of food.

The herd of sambar deer were grazing peacefully on vegetation in the shallow water, unaware that a lone male tiger was stalking them. The predator had to creep to within 60ft (18m) before rushing suddenly from the bushes and chasing into the water. The herd scatters and a youngster, less able to escape, is caught and killed with a suffocating bite to the neck. The tiger will drag its meal to the bushes on the lake shore and consume it at leisure.

'Save the Tiger' has been both a conservation success story and a nightmare. Tiger populations have increased, but their living space has contracted. With limited supplies of wild food, tigers have turned to killing livestock (like the cow in the photo left) and even people.

In the Sunderbanns Tiger Reserve in West Bengal, India, attacks on local people have prompted some novel attempts to scare away tigers. This mannequin, dressed as a woodcutter, is wired to give an attacking tiger an electric shock. It is hoped that the unpleasant surprise will discourage tigers from stalking and killing local woodcutters and fishermen.

An angry warthog is a formidable foe for a solitary leopard. Short, sharp tusks in the lower jaw could seriously injure the big cat, and so the leopard may take up to 2 hours to exhaust and subdue its prey. More usually a leopard will go for a quick kill.

Leopards often have their hard-earned meal stolen from them by lions or hyenas and so they haul the carcass high into a tree. They drink the blood and will sometimes pluck the fur or feathers from prey before starting to eat.

▲

Thick-furred snow leopards have a hard time in the harsh conditions that prevail in the central Asian mountains in which they live. Prey includes bharal (blue sheep), markhor (the largest goat), marmots and domestic livestock. They can outrun their prey over snow and make leaps of up to 40ft (13m) over rocks.

◄

The jaguar resembles the leopard, its fur patterned with spots and rosettes, but it is restricted to South and Central America. It is stockier, with shorter legs and tail, an adaptation to its jungle lifestyle. It is a fine swimmer and is often found near water. The most common food item in Belize is the armadillo, while in the Matto Grosso of Brazil the capybara is the favourite prey.

The polar bear of the Arctic is a giant, vying with the Kodiak bear for the title of world's largest terrestrial carnivore. This invidivual is waiting patiently at a hole in the ice where seals come up to breathe. The next one to visit the hole is in for a terrible surprise, for the bear will swipe with its forepaw and hook it out of the water in an instant.

Having caught their prey - often ringed seals, the smallest and commonest seals in the Arctic - polar bears eat mainly the flesh and blubber. They can consume about 88lb (40kg) at one sitting, the leftovers providing a meal for the scavengers, such as Arctic foxes and skuas.

◄

A white-bellied sea eagle swoops over the water, its legs and talons ready to reach out and snatch a fish at the surface.

▼

Ospreys are found all over the world. They catch fish at the water's surface by plunging into the water, their talons outstretched. This osprey in Florida has been successful. It carried the fish torpedo-fashion, with the head end first in order to reduce drag while flying, and has returned to a favourite perch in order to feed.

Co-operative Hunting

2

Solitary hunters often go hungry, but with a little help from the family a predator can increase greatly its chances of obtaining a meal.

Teamwork also ensures that prey, once killed, is not stolen. Rival hunting teams and scavengers are ready to lift a prize from right under a predator's nose. An alert group is a strong deterrent. Lions may be large and powerful creatures, but a solitary lion at a kill is more than likely to be harassed by a pack of cheeky hyenas and lose its hard-earned dinner. Hyenas are more cautious about attacking an entire pride.

Co-operation requires communication. For a team to perform well, the team members must speak to each other, using sounds, body language, smells and touch. They must understand the social niceties of working within a well-honed group, know their status and play their role without shirking. Squabbles must be avoided or the team becomes less effective. Each individual is dependent on the rest of the team for the entire group to succeed. Not surprisingly, all co-operative hunters have well-developed channels of communication and ritualised behaviour for establishing a group hierarchy. Most hunting groups have a leader, a dominant animal to which all group members pay their respects. Sometimes it is a male, but often it is an alpha female, the only female in the group permitted to breed.

One of the major disadvantages of co-operative hunting is that the prey must be shared and each individual in the group receives less food than if it hunted alone. Animals, therefore, must balance the advantages of hunting in a group with those of hunting alone. Some have it both ways. They hunt communally when prey is scarce or too large to kill unaided, and singly when prey is small or plentiful.

A PRIDE OF LIONS

LIONS ARE LAZY beasts. For most of the day, they loll around sleeping, scratching or staring. Hunting is carried out by the females, the dominant adult males taking no part. Their role is to guard the pride and keep it safe. A large pride may consist of a pair of fully grown males, 6 lionesses and a dozen cubs of various ages between 10 and 14 months. The hunting territory of a pride on, say, the Serengeti Plains in East Africa can extend to 54 square miles (140 square km), while nomadic groups may travel 1,500 miles (3,885km) in a year, following the vast herds of wildebeest on their extensive migrations.

Hunting begins at sunset. The resident pride take an interest in the endless, weaving line of wildebeest. The pace of these ungulates is leisurely; there is no obvious threat. The lions watch passively from a knoll, eyes and ears alert. The flick of a tail betrays an intention. The pride becomes tense. They are going hunting.

Without ceremony, one of the females leaves the group. The wildebeest have stopped to graze and do not notice. Unseen, the lioness makes her way around the parade, a flanking movement designed to cut off their escape. As one, the other females yawn, stretch and casually slip down between the tufts of savannah grass. The hunt is on.

Each lioness flattens her profile, bellies are pressed to the floor, heads remain steady. A bull wildebeest snorts and looks up. The team freezes. Only a row of ears can be seen above the long grass stems. The flanking lioness is invisible but ready. The wind is favourable for the attackers; it is blowing towards them. The wildebeest resume feeding.

Already a victim has been selected - a vulnerable youngster or an old or infirm adult. Somehow each lioness knows which it is. Its behaviour has been observed and noted, and it has been targeted by the pride.

Slowly, the lionesses creep towards the unsuspecting prey. Any sudden

Mature male lions are lazy. As sub-adults they would have caught their own food, but when they take over the pride they let the lionesses do the chasing about. When the prey is caught and killed, the pride's males have the first bite and the choicest cuts. The rest of the pride eat what is left.

CO-OPERATION FOR SUCCESS

A solitary African lion, with an interest in dining out on Thompson's gazelles - the ubiquitous prey animal of the African savannah (every predator seems to try for them) - makes a catch in only 15 per cent of attempts. A small group of 2-4 animals does better with a 32 per cent success rate. Lions in a large hunting pride are twice as likely to be successful than an animal that hunts alone. Combined effort and co-operation increase hunting success. There are clear survival benefits, and many animals, including lions, hyenas, African hunting dogs, dholes, dolphins and killer whales, have discovered the gastronomic advantages to be gained by hunting in a well-organised team.

movement, any sign of alertness among the wildebeest, and the pride stops, waits, then resumes its slow, methodical advance. Lions are stalkers. They must get to within 100ft (30m) of the target before bolting from cover. A lioness at full tilt can reach 36mph (58km/h) for a short distance, but many prey animals can run faster and for longer. Stealth is the answer, and surprise is vital.

The main wave of attackers is close to the critical point at which they must break cover. Suddenly, at some hidden signal, they explode on to the plain. The startled wildebeest and the zebra accompanying them first scatter in all directions, but then run with the herd. The pride stampedes them this way and that, and in the confusion the target animal is isolated. It runs wild and fast, but something about it is wrong; it has a slight, almost undetectable limp, the result of hitting a pothole during a previous attack. Nevertheless, it is faster than the lionesses.

Suddenly, the flanking lioness jumps from behind a bush and confronts the frightened wildebeest. It is stronger than it looks and is determined to live. Head down, it charges the lioness. She jumps aside, drops to the ground and rolls on her back, paws in the air. The wildebeest, sensing an advantage, bears down on her exposed underside with its heavy horns. This is what she has been waiting for. With a twist of her body, she wraps her forepaws around the wildebeest's neck and topples it on its side. At the same moment she sinks her teeth into its neck. As it writhes and suffocates in the vice-like grip, the rest of the lionesses fall upon it and disembowel it.

In the distance, one of the pride's lions is running towards the now limp carcass. His shaggy mane, designed to make him look even bigger and more powerful than he already is, flies in the slipstream. With a loud snarl, he scatters the hunters and takes his position over the choicest cut. The females gather at the other end of the carcass. Gradually, the rest of the pride, including cubs and juveniles, arrives. The cubs are last to feed - they are well down the hierarchy, but they too will eventually eat their fill. The pride rests, the hunt is over.

THE HYENA SISTERHOOD

SPOTTED HYENAS ARE brutish in appearance, but they are a sisterhood of female killers. They mainly hunt together at night. They will catch or steal almost anything and eat almost everything they have caught, including bones, horns, hooves and hair. They are the 'dustbins' of Africa, digesting bones and regurgitating indigestible matter in a pellet. Ultra-strong jaws and sharp teeth can tear flesh and sever bones. A clan of 38 hyenas was seen to rip apart and devour a full-grown zebra carcass in only 15 minutes. Little was left but a stain on the ground.

Hyenas are not only scavengers, but also powerful hunters. A solitary hyena can chase an adult wildebeest for a distance of 3 miles (5km), at speeds of up to 37mph (60km/h) and bring the beast down alone. Stamina and speed, rather than stealth, bring results. Clans of 10-15 hyenas can tackle the much larger and stronger zebra, and in the Serengeti clans of 50 or more are reported.

The clan leader is always female and so are the senior members of the clan. The males, which are noticeably smaller than the females, have a very low social status, but curiously the female mimics them to the extent of having a penis-like structure similar to that of the male. Both sexes have the same powerful forequarters, with front legs longer than the back, and the steeply-sloping back - for witches to ride on, according to local folklore.

When spotted hyenas meet, they protrude their anal gland in greeting and lift a

A lioness hunts with her sisters and other close relatives, in order to bring down large animals like zebra. While one of the pride crawls unobtrusively behind the target animals to prevent them escaping, the rest of the group stalks slowly forwards until it is time to break from cover and start the chase.

hind leg so that they can lick and sniff each other's genitals. This behaviour, in hyena terms, is both security pass and membership card rolled into one. The anal gland also produces a pungent creamy paste, known locally as 'witches' butter'. This is rubbed on to grass stems at hyena-nose height as a semi-permanent territorial scent mark, a warning to other hyena clans to keep out. Each hyena produces its own individual scent. Territorial boundaries are also marked by communal urination and defecation sites.

When on the move, clan members call constantly to one another, making whoop-calls, yelps and demoniacal cackles. Each hyena has its own distinctive voice.

Headquarters tends to be a vacated aardvark burrow and during the day the clan rests close-by. As dusk falls, the clan begins to stretch and limber up. There is a roll call, with much sniffing and lifting of legs, but when the greetings reach fever pitch the clan is ready to hunt. Their target for the night is a herd of zebra. But hyena eyes are not the only ones watching the prey; lions are watching too.

The hyenas close in on the herd. They run with their tails erect, scattering the

herd. In the confusion, a zebra foal is singled out. With a yelp, the leading hyenas pounce on it, warily dodging the wild kicks of the mother's razor-sharp hooves. The mother and a nearby stallion charge the hyenas, but it is too late. The clan regroup and overwhelm the foal. The mother joins the rest of the herd, which stampedes this way and that in panic.

The lions, meanwhile, sense an opportunity for surprise. The mother zebra does not see them coming. A lioness pounces and brings her down. Not far away, her foal is already a disembowelled and dismembered carcass. The hyenas eat their fill, finishing every scrap. The fastest eaters take the most - a hyena can eat one third of its body weight at a single sitting. But the zebra foal was small and the hyenas are still hungry. The lions, settling down for their midnight feast, are in for a surprise visit.

Encouraged by the whoop-calls that echoed across the dark plain, other clan members come running. They sense that the second carcass could also be theirs. They gather round the lions, taunting them with yelps and cackles. Three young lions have taken a large chunk of zebra to one side. The hyenas concentrate their

The lion may be the king of beasts, but the hyena is the prince of thieves. Three lionesses are chased from their kill by a pack of spotted hyenas. The lions will have put up a brave fight, but the sheer numbers of hyenas will have put the lions to flight.

efforts on them - they are more easily intimidated than their elders. The hyenas make their charge, momentarily scattering the young lions. In seconds the hyenas make off with the prize.

But lions must never be underestimated. Making the most of a careless moment, a large male lion rushes at the hyenas, grabbing one of them by the throat. The hyena slowly suffocates. The clan retreats; there are youngsters to be fed.

WILD DOGS OF AFRICA

WHERE LIONS RELY on stealth and hyenas on brute force, African wild dogs are known for their stamina and determination. They hunt mainly in the coolness of dawn and dusk, but may be active throughout an overcast day and during a bright moonlit night. They are plains hunters, depending on sight to spot their quarry amongst a herd of antelope, often impala and springbok. One victim is selected and the pack moves in. Throughout the hunt, the dogs will stick like glue to the chosen prey, wearing it down until the time is right for the kill.

With the quarry isolated, two dogs begin the chase. The rest of the pack lopes along comfortably, fanning out behind the pursuit. As the first chasers tire, they return to the pack and a second pair set out to take their place. The pattern is repeated time after time, the prey chased relentlessly at speeds of up to 45mph (70km/h). Eventually, terror and fatigue combine to weaken the prey. As it

African wild dogs are relatively small and must co-operate closely to bring down large prey. While some dogs try to grab the ears or lips, others attach themselves to the rear of the prey. Eventually, it is weakened and falls under the weight of sheer numbers of dogs.

slows, imperceptibly to the human eye, the dogs know that the end is near. The chaser dogs go in, jumping at the flanks and belly, tearing away chunks of flesh, and weakening the victim further from loss of blood. It is not a clean kill, the unfortunate target eventually stumbling to the ground, entrails sometimes spread across the savannah floor. In an instant and in a sudden explosion of excited high-pitched chattering, the pack tears at the corpse. A medium-sized impala is devoured completely in less than 10 minutes, the hurried feast accompanied by growls and whines. If the prey is small and the pack big, the dogs are on their feet once more and alert to the chance of another meal. Unlike the other plains animals, hunting dogs rarely scavenge, but when desperate from hunger they have been known to chase a solitary lion from its kill.

In some regions, wild dogs have learned how co-operation can land them bigger prizes. Zebras, for instance, are powerful animals and hunting dogs tend to leave them alone. There is, however, a lot of meat on an adult zebra, enough to feed a large pack well. And on the Serengeti Plains in Tanzania, wild dogs have learned how to bring down such an animal without receiving injuries from the hooves.

The basic hunting technique is the same. The zebra is chased until it is tired, but then the dogs adopt a new approach. Instead of first going for the flanks and getting kicked, one dog grabs and hangs on to the tail and another bites on to the upper lip. Both hang on tight, while the rest of the pack attacks the vulnerable underside and disembowels the prey. Using this technique as few as four dogs can overpower a zebra, an animal ten times the size of each dog.

The strategy, interestingly, is learned. Young dogs watch and learn from their parents. The behaviour is confined to just two groups of dogs, and they have been doing it for the past 10 years through 3 successive generations.

THE COMPANY OF WOLVES

A PACK OF WOLVES is a highly co-ordinated, disciplined and efficient killing unit. In winter, the prey of timber wolves living in the coniferous forests of North America tends to be caribou, moose and deer; in summer, hares, beavers and rodents are staples of the wolf diet.

Packs vary in size, depending on the prey. In moose country, large packs of up to 20 animals are common. Deer hunting packs tend to be smaller, with 7 or 8

Grey wolves once roamed over much of the land in the northern hemisphere, but today they are restricted to the wilder parts of Alaska, Canada and Siberia. Small populations also survive in national parks in the USA, Italy, Yugoslavia, Romania, Poland, Czechoslovakia, Bulgaria, Greece, Spain, Portugal and the Indian sub-continent.

animals. Leading every pack is an alpha pair, a dominant male and female. They are the only breeding animals in the pack. The home range can be anything between 40 and 400 square miles (100-1,000 square km), and to find food the pack may have to travel up to 32 miles (50km) a day. Neighbouring packs seldom fight and actively avoid confrontation. By setting up a chorus of howls before and after a kill, a pack signals its size and fierceness to other packs. In fact, researchers have found that smaller packs use the echoes and reverberations of wolf howls, bouncing off trees and foliage as they pass through the forest, to fool other packs that they are bigger than they really are.

The hunt is usually preceded by a group howl, with much greeting, nuzzling and nose-pushing. Then the pack moves off, in single file. Its chance of success depends on the size, speed and defensive tactics of its prey. A deer in its prime is well able to outrun a wolf pack. A healthy moose is likely to stand its ground,

When hunting dogs return to the den site, the youngsters are waiting for them. They each approach an adult and begin to lick its face. The licking causes the adult to regurgitate some meat for the pup. The dog cannot help itself for its response is automatic.

forcing the pack to back off - only one in twelve moose hunts end in a kill. Musk oxen will form a defensive phalanx, or karre. When wolves threaten, the herd shuffles and reels as one, adults with their heads facing the threat and youngsters safely tucked in behind. The wolves' only chance of success, faced with an almost impenetrable wall of hooves and horns, is to panic the herd and make it run, picking off any youngster that is left behind.

All predators, wolves included, are expert at spotting the best targets, usually the young, the old and the sick. Sometimes a wolf pack will chase a deer for several miles, but on other occasions the chase is quickly abandoned. Something in the way the deer runs indicates whether it is catchable or not.

Wolves lack the killing, suffocating bite of the big cats. Their method is to dodge in and tear pieces out of the flanks and belly of their prey. When the animal can no longer keep going, the entire pack piles in and tears it to pieces. Moose-hunting tactics are slightly different. Because a direct blow from the front hoof of a moose can kill a wolf, one wolf goes for the moose's nose and hangs on regardless. Wolves have solved their problem in the same way as certain wild dog packs in Africa. The behaviour prevents the moose from lashing out with its front hooves, while the rest of the pack attacks the rear.

Once the prey has been downed, there is another howling ceremony. This acts like a beacon in the wilderness, allowing animals that have become separated from the pack during the chase to catch up. A roll call of howls ensures that the whole pack is present before the feast begins. If food is scarce, as it usually is in winter, nothing will remain uneaten. If the carcass is too big to eat at one sitting, the remainder will be cached in the snow to be eaten later.

In early summer, when cubs are being reared, one or two yearlings and older pack members stay behind to guard the den site while the rest are away hunting. When the hunters return, stomachs full, the pups lick their muzzles to elicit regurgitation of the meat they have eaten. The licking triggers an automatic, uncontrolled response. In fact, pups often mob returning wolves to such an extent that they quickly re-eat the meat they have regurgitated as if they hadn't really meant to 'cough up' in the first place.

THE DHOLE PACK - DAWN RAIDERS

THE DHOLE OR RED DOG is the wild dog of Asia and it has the reputation throughout its range as a cruel and vicious killer. It too is a pack animal, living and hunting in groups of up to 20 animals, although smaller packs are more common. A typical Indian pack consists of 8 adults and as many pups, all produced by the same dominant female. An average home range covers an area of about 15 square miles (40 square km), with boundaries marked by latrine sites where the dhole pack urinates and defecates together.

Dholes hunt during the day and sometimes on moonlit nights. The first hunt begins at dawn. The animals stand or sit in a clearing, calling intermittently in what seems to be a roll call and pep talk. When all have indicated that they are ready, the pack moves off through the long grass. The leader, a dominant male, stops and sniffs the air, then freezes: he has picked up the scent of a chital deer. One of the pack jumps into the air, trying to see over the grass. Another stands on its hind legs. The herd is not far away.

The pack adopts hunting strategy 1. They fan out through the grass in line abreast. The first dhole to make contact with the prey will initiate the attack. The cue for the others to join in will be the alarm call of the deer and the sound of the chase. Eyes and ears alert, the pack moves forward.

Suddenly, the alarm call is heard and the deer bound away into the nearby forest. Running like the wind, the pack converges on the position of the first attacker and gives chase, but the target deer are too fast. Before too much energy is wasted, the pack leader calls off the attack. Whistles fill the air and the pack reassembles.

Time for hunting strategy 2. While the rest of the pack waits at the forest edge, two dholes trot off into the trees. Their job is to flush out the prey and drive it towards the others.

Again, the alarm call is heard. Suddenly, a lone chital stag erupts from the forest, hotly pursued by the stalker. Seeing the ambush ahead, the stag stops and the

pursuing dholes attack from behind. Knocked momentarily off balance, the stag falls. In an instant, the ambushers pounce, disembowel it, and, even before the prey is dead, the pack starts to eat. The animal eventually dies from shock and loss of blood. Heart, liver and eyeballs are dhole delicacies and are devoured first, but there are no squabbles. Competition is confined to who can eat the fastest. A dhole can bolt down 9lb (4kg) of meat in one sitting.

When the meal is over, the pack heads for water. Dholes drink as frequently as they eat, and often sit for hours in streams and pools to keep cool.

Dholes work together to catch antelope, wild boar and wild sheep. They will also try for small rodents and will eat carrion. Like other dogs, all the dhole adults in a pack bring back food for the youngsters.

BEWARE DOLPHINS

AT SOME TIME in the remote past, a group of terrestrial hunting mammals returned to the sea, evolving into the dolphins and toothed whales we know today. Dolphins are descended from terrestrial carnivores and, like co-operative cats and dogs, they hunt together. They herd fish into bays, using the surface of the sea as a 'wall' to restrict the number of escape routes. They use sound to direct the fish, and the dolphin school swims around and below the fish in an ever-tightening formation. The more dolphins present, the better the fishing. A school of 5-10 are not best to herd a fish shoal, and the attack will be aborted after 5 minutes. A 50-strong group, however, can feed for half an hour, and a school with 300 dolphins might feed for 2-3 hours depending on the availability of prey.

The Gulf of California is home to common dolphins. Imagine a day with no wind, and the surface of the sea is mirror-calm. In the distance the cries of Heerman's gulls cut the stillness. Suddenly, there is the sound of rushing water and the surface of the sea begins to boil with hundreds of leaping, charging common dolphins, their intricate side-stripes clearly visible. They are hunting sardines.

Common dolphins travel the seas in large schools. These 9ft-long (3m) dolphins, with characteristic stripes along the side of the body, follow traditional routes, arriving at particular places when their prey is seasonally plentiful.

Sardines move around the Gulf of California, following upwellings of cool, nutrient-rich water. As the winds reverse in summer and winter, prey and predators switch sides, and with the migrating shoals of sardines go huge schools of common dolphins and smaller congregations of Bryde's whales. Whereas the whales simply take huge gulps of seawater and sardines, and filter out the water through their baleen plates, common dolphins have 200 sharply pointed, backward-curving teeth to ensure that the slippery little fish do not escape. Both species herd sardines, concentrating them into dense shoals, and then dash through them to feed. The dolphins spray the fish with high-density beams of ultra-high-frequency sound, debilitating them and scooping them up with ease.

Dolphins are normally noisy creatures, communicating with one another by a series of clicks, whistles and burps. But occasionally, when the sea is very calm and visibility is good, they seem to navigate in silence. Whether they are listening for the ocean's natural echoes, the sound signatures of seamounts and canyons, or silently taking compass headings from the sun is unknown.

Common dolphins are not confined to the California gulf, but are found all over the world in temperate and sub-tropical seas. Schools can contain many animals. A school spotted from a ship en route to Dakar was reported to have been 'millions' strong, while another off New Zealand was credited to occupy a section of sea 32 miles (51km) long and half-a-mile wide. Schools with 200,000 dolphins have been seen catching anchovies and sprats in the Black Sea. They are also deep divers. Common dolphins regularly dive to 200ft in search of smelt and lantern fish. One individual was recorded to have dived to 846ft.

SPINNERS OF HAWAII

HAWAIIAN SPINNER DOLPHINS hunt in the Pacific Ocean at night and return to the islands each day to rest and recuperate. Everything they do, they do together. At dawn, large schools split into smaller groups as they approach the islands and spend the day in sheltered bays. In the late afternoon, activity increases and the noise level rises. Individuals swim back and forth whistling and clicking. The whistles are thought to be individual signatures and each dolphin is announcing it is present and ready for action.

At the surface, dolphins begin to leap clear of the water, spinning as they go and crashing back in a hugh splash. Below they roll over and around each other, constantly calling; the more activity, the more noise.

Suddenly, some individuals begin to swim in a zig-zag fashion. They move slowly to the entrance of the bay and then rapidly back to the school. It is as if they cannot decide whether it is time to go or not. The sounds come and go. One dolphin calls and the others reply. The sounds seem to indicate how unified the group feels. When all the dolphins chime in at the appropriate time, the group is ready to hunt.

By late afternoon leaping, tail slapping and calling reaches a peak, and at some hidden signal the school heads for the open sea. About a mile from the shore the school meets other groups and the enlarged school, sometimes 100 strong, begins to hunt. Throughout the night, the schools coalesce and split, with individuals swapping groups. They fan out in line abreast scanning the ocean ahead with their echolocation sounds. They dive deep, down to 300ft or more, where they find and feed on shoals of fish.

In the morning, they head for the islands and the daily pattern of activity starts all over again.

WHALES CALLED ORCA

FOR CENTURIES MAN has been in awe of the orca. Its reputation can be judged from its many names: the Romans called it 'orca' after an underworld ogre; the Scandinavians know it as 'blubber chopper'; the Spanish call it 'assassin'; and in English it is the killer whale, a name derived from a savage reputation as the only whale to devour warm-blooded prey.

Although given the name 'whale', the orca is the largest of the dolphins, a supercetacean that can grow to 30ft (9m) long and weigh 9 tonnes, which is about the same size as a single-decker bus. It is one of the swiftest animals in the sea, able to outswim and outmanoeuvre its prey - one of the sea's supreme predators.

Orca society is matriarchal. Each pod consists of up to 20 individuals, all related to each other through the two or three mothers and one or two grannies that dominate the group. The rest are juveniles, youngsters and bulls. Although much larger than the cows, the bulls are of inferior status.

Sometimes a pod travels together; at other times, small sub-groups split off to pursue prey not worthy of the attention of the entire group. The smaller groups always return to the main pod and so, in the long term, orca society remains stable.

In one orca study area, off the coast of British Columbia near Vancouver Island, scientists have identified two kinds of orca: residents and transients, which look and behave differently. The residents have a slender, rounded dorsal fin, travel in pods of up to 30 whales, and are most active when the Pacific salmon return to their home rivers to spawn. Their lifestyle is determined by the behaviour of their prey.

Salmon swim in large mobile shoals, a food source that is said to be 'clumped'. In order to find a 'clump', it is an advantage to have a large group which can spread out and, working together, search a wide area of ocean.

When hunting, the whales spread out in a line-abreast search formation, each whale positioning itself about 150ft (50m) from its neighbour. The line advances slowly, the whales constantly 'talking' to each other in squeals and moans. At the sound of a loud honk, the pod converges on the salmon and herds them towards a cove, trapping them against the shore. Fish on the periphery of the shoal are picked off one by one. Then, as suddenly as it began, the attack is called off. The whales submerge, swim further along the coast, and repeat their herding and feeding behaviour all over again.

Transient whales, which have a stubby, triangular dorsal fin, are less predictable in their behaviour and travel inshore to feed on more thinly dispersed and less abundant sources of food. The transient hunt is more dramatic, the pod taking seals and sea-lions instead of fish. A small pod will round up a group of sea-lions, isolate a victim, and then butt it with their powerful tails until it is unconscious. This may take a couple of hours, after which the prey is taken below, drowned and eaten. Despite its size, the orca is a cautious predator. A bite or scratch from a large seal could inflict serious damage.

Orca diets vary considerably. Off Japan, orcas feed on cod and halibut; near the Brazilian coast, they eat stingrays; and in the northern Pacific, sea-lions, elephant seals and other dolphins are fair game. This is how one eye-witness described a co-operative attack on a group of dolphins: 'The killers must have heard their chatter and closed in silently, intent on the kill. They had formed a circle round the dolphins and then they moved steadily in, closing the circle, driving the hapless dolphins before them into a crowded ring. When the killer circle had decreased to about fifty metres across, the dolphins swimming round nose to tail, three or four of the hunters entered the enclosure and selected as many victims as they needed to satisfy their hunger. These they maimed, biting some across the tail so they could not swim away.'

The most spectacular orca attacks ever observed have involved the great baleen whales. Grey whales, migrating along the Pacific coast of North America, are followed by pods of orcas. Humpback whales, which feed off the coasts of Newfoundland and Alaska, are mercilessly pursued. As always, the victims are often the young, the old and the infirm. Another eye-witness account tells of a 5-hour struggle between orcas and a blue whale, the world's largest living creature: 'The predators exhibited marked divisions of labour. Some flanked the blue on either side, as if herding it. Two others went ahead and stayed behind to foil any escape attempts. One group seemed intent on keeping the blue underwater to hinder its breathing. Another phalanx swam underneath its belly to make sure it didn't dive out of reach. The big whale's dorsal fin had been chewed off and its tail flukes shredded, impairing its movements. The bulls led forays to pull off huge chunks of flesh.' Miraculously, the whale survived and eventually got away.

Young southern sea-lions on Patagonian beaches may not be so lucky. In this area, orcas have learned to charge ashore, coming right out of the water, grab a victim and shuffle back into the sea. Any individual careless enough to stay in the target zone is in mortal danger. The orcas are unexpectedly fast and surprisingly well practised. During the penguin breeding season, when sea-lions are making offshore feeding forays of their own in search of penguins, the orcas have been seen to practise their beach-charging skills on steeply shelving beaches similar to those frequented by the sea-lions during their breeding season. The young whales learn from their elders, the technique standing them in good stead for the whales are able to take 20 sea-lions in an hour.

The sea-lions seem frozen to the spot, mesmerised and confused by the great black-and-white shape that emerges from the water and grabs them on dry land. And the terror does not end there. The orcas tend not to eat their prey immediately. Instead they 'play' with it, much like a cat playing with a mouse. Using their great muscular tail, they lob the sea-lions, young and old alike, up to 20ft in the air. And they do this again and again.

Young sea-lions in the 'danger zone' on a Patagonian coast are snatched by killer whales or orcas. The whales have learned to swim in the shallow surf and beach themselves in order to reach their victims. They then manoeuvre themselves back into the water and often 'play' with their prey - thwacking it continually into the air with their powerful tail.

The bottlenose dolphin is the species most commonly seen in dolphinaria. In the wild, it is found all over the world. This group is swimming off the Australian coast. In order to travel with the minimum of effort, dolphins sometimes catch a ride on the bow waves of boats, a throwback probably to the habit of riding on the bow waves of large whales.

A pod of orcas or killer whales pass through the Chatham Straits in south-east Alaska. They co-ordinate their activities by calls - mostly squeals, whistles, clicks and burps - which are specific to each pod. Those pods that catch fish, such as salmon returning to their home rivers, are very noisy even when hunting. But those pods that hunt seals and sea-lions conduct their hunt in silence lest they alert their prey.

The killer whale is the largest of the dolphin family. It is one of the 'toothed' whales. Its jaws are lined with peg-like teeth for grabbing prey. It catches fish, from salmon to large sharks, and warm-blooded prey, from seals to giant baleen whales.

Spotted hyenas must hunt together in order to bring down a buffalo (below). They might also steal a meal from a pride of lions, and in turn have their food stolen from them by a bunch of vultures (right). With luck, an individual might be left alone for long enough to eat its food, but it must be quick to gorge down its fill. Hyenas eat everything on the carcass, including bones and hair.

Lions kill by suffocation. The predator grabs the prey (a wildebeest) by the throat and constricts the windpipe so that the animal cannot breathe (below). Lions in the Kalahari kill gemsbock by breaking the lower vertebral column. Whatever the method, the resulting carcass is shared by the entire pride (left). Male lions have first choice and cubs are last in line. When prey is scarce, there is sometimes little food left and cubs can go hungry.

Timber or grey wolves at a kill. Young, old or injured moose, deer and caribou, which are much larger than the wolf itself, are commonly caught by well-organised packs. Hares and beavers are caught in summer, but in winter, when snow is deep, it is more difficult to catch prey and farm stock or carrion can be on the menu. This pack, from Montana, USA, has brought down a white-tailed deer (below).

The dhole of South and South-East Asia may have exclusive hunting rights in an area of about 15 square miles (40sq km). The pack calls to each other in whines, growls, barks and whistles. The whistle reassembles the pack after an aborted hunt.

The Gang

3

Gangs are a little less sophisticated than the dedicated co-operative hunters. Sheer enthusiasm, a little cunning and supperiority of numbers often win the day. Unlike the stealthy, silent approach of the serious trackers, gangs tend to be noisy, less organised and rely to some extent on luck. They often panic the prey, a strategy that disorientates and confuses, making prey animals more vulnerable to being caught.

It is not often clear whether a loose gang is actually hunting together. Members of the group may take an interest in the hunting activity of their colleagues, but whether the resulting hunt could be considered true co-operation is debatable. It could be that the observed pooling of effort is simply a number of selfish individuals trying to capture the same item of prey.

Gangs are also an insurance against the predators themselves becoming the prey of other predators. Small animals such as mongooses and meerkats forage in groups, but actually tackle food, such as scorpions, individually. Where lions and jackals have joined together to increase hunting success, mongooses favour gang living for mutual defence. The many watchful eyes and alert ears in a group are constantly searching for foxes and eagles that might take a plump meerkat, and the assembled gang can effectively deal collectively with an intruding poisonous snake.

HUNTING RELATIVES

CHIMPANZEES, LIKE HUMANS, are opportunists. They eat fruit, stems, bark, leaves and roots. They crack open nuts using branches and rocks as nut-crackers, and they fish with twigs for termites and ants. But occasionally they go hunting, and when they do it is a blood-chilling spectacle.

Prey animals might include small antelope, wild pigs and monkeys, a particular favourite being colobus monkeys. The monkeys are safe as long as the forest canopy is continuous and there are plenty of escape routes through the trees. After all, colobus monkeys are light and agile and able to travel along arboreal highways denied chimpanzees. Chimps are not good leapers and can only progress through the trees when they can swing easily from one branch to the next. But if the canopy is broken and escape routes are few, the monkeys must be wary for the chimpanzees are likely to launch a surprise attack. In West

GANG WARFARE

By joining a gang, an animal has a better chance of bringing down its prey. Some degree of co-operation also enables animals that normally do not hunt to be able to set out and catch a meal that would ordinarily be denied them. There is, however, a price to pay. In the free-for-all that follows a gang hunt there might not be enough meat for all. Gangs are not generally noted for fairness when it comes to sharing the spoils. Predators that mainly hunt alone, occasionally hunt with others. Canadian lynx will spread out in a line and drive through a forest, frightening hares from cover. The nearest cat to the prey takes the prize. And pairs of lynx will work in harmony, one cat frightening the prey towards the other.

A troop (which may consist of 12-50 individuals) of banded mongooses forages together in search of insects, snails, ground-breeding birds, lizards and snakes. A large, poisonous snake will be tackled by the group fighting as one.

Grey meerkats or suricates stand on the hind legs and scan the skies for dangerous eagles. As a group they sometimes catch baby hares, but more often forage for insects and spiders, scorpions, birds' eggs, lizards and snakes.

African rainforests chimpanzees eat meat at least once a week.

To achieve their weekly goal chimpanzees must hunt together. Superior intelligence and a degree of co-operation ensure that they can manipulate the movements of the monkey troop and at the end of the hunt catch their prey. Not all the chimpanzees in a party take part in the hunt - usually half-a-dozen adult males - and each has its role to play. The youngest moves along behind the monkeys preventing them from settling and slowly moves the troop forwards. The oldest finds a place in the forest ahead where he can ambush the prey moving towards him. Flankers, on either side of the troop, ensure the sides of the trap are covered and that the monkeys are unable to escape that way.

The hunt starts with slow but deliberate movements, the chimpanzees travelling on the ground. The normal group chatter stops and the chimpanzees move in silence. They search the branches for the monkeys above, and when the other members of the hunt are in place a couple of the more agile chimps race up the trees. They pick out one or two isolated monkeys and begin the chase. The colobus flee, heading straight for the old ambusher ahead. At the right moment, he reveals himself and the colobus panic. They cannot go on and they cannot escape to either side. In that moment of indecision, the chimpanzees pounce and, with blood-curdling shrieks, proclaim to the group waiting below that they have caught a colobus. The rest, mainly females and youngsters, join the chorus until the forest is filled with terrifying sounds of screams, pant-hoots and barks. The calls tell all the troop that the food has been caught and the hunt is over. Outlying chimps home-in on the callers.

The highest-ranking males tear the still-living monkey apart. The pieces are distributed to lesser-ranking males and females. Sometimes, the screaming prey is eviscerated before being brought to the ground. Other methods of killing include biting into the head or whirling the body about until the head smashes against a rock or branch. A large animal, such as a juvenile bush-pig, may have its legs broken by slamming it against a tree. It may not die until much later, when it is slowly torn apart. Its final scream reverberates through the forest as its heart is torn from its body.

Chimpanzees hunt a variety of prey, including young bush-pigs, baby baboons, bushbuck fawns, mice, rats and small birds. Human infants have also been taken - a woman gathering firewood in Tanzania had a baby snatched from her back, and a 6-year-old boy was captured by chimpanzees - and cannibalism is known to occur.

BULLY BOYS OF THE RAINFOREST

MANDRILLS, WEARING RED, blue and white stripes on their face, like gaudy intimidating war-paint, are formidable and unexpectedly ferocious predators. They gather in enormous groups, containing 50-150 individuals, and bring terror to the West African rainforest. Their hunting behaviour is reminiscent of the antics of human teenagers. The most recent manifestation of urban deprivation is the phenomenon of 'wilding'. Gangs of delinquents rush through shopping malls, scaring customers, terrorising shopkeepers and stealing goods. The behaviour resembles closely the way mandrills and their small cousins, the drills, hunt in the wild.

A large group of up to 100 mandrills runs screaming into the forest. Females and young males act as flushers and flankers, channelling a 100-metre-wide swathe of devastation through the open forest. There is little undergrowth and

Mandrills are omnivorous, but hunt for meat regularly - sometimes once a day in the dry season. They live on the forest floor of west central Africa, in primary rainforest between the Niger and Congo rivers. Only males have brightly coloured faces.

the drills are able to move quickly. Terrified prey scatters in all directions, often running blindly into the advancing line of alpha males, the butchers of the group. Antelope, monkeys and virtually anything else that moves are quickly dispatched or disabled, their gory corpses left on the ground. The predators continue their onslaught, not stopping to feed, but killing every living thing in their path. At a given signal, the hunt is called off and the mandrills scour the battlefield for dead and dying animals. The huge troop settles down to feed.

On the savannah of southern and East Africa, olive baboons co-operate to some degree to take young gazelles and hares that lie hidden in the grass. The troop spreads out and, like beaters at a grouse shoot, flush the prey from cover. Whether baboons gain any advantage by hunting together is questionable. Solo hunters are just as successful as those hunting in a group. But whatever the method, team spirit certainly breaks down when a victim is caught. A possessive and dominant baboon is reluctant to share its catch with the rest of the group.

Baboons, like chimpanzees, however, do call after a hunt and, where baboons and chimpanzees share the same stretch of forest or savannah, the baboon calls will bring the chimps running. The chimpanzees then steal the meat.

COYOTE WESTERN

COYOTES ARE ALSO OPPORTUNISTS, and the size of the available prey determines whether they hunt alone or in small packs. Rodents are caught by lone coyotes; after all, there is not enough meat on a mouse to feed two or more. A solitary coyote, pouncing on voles in North America, has a hard time. Five of these fast-moving rodents will escape before the coyote gets its meal. It has a better chance with ground squirrels; for every five ground squirrels it attempts to catch, it succeeds with two.

But the availability of elk or deer demands a more concerted effort and degree of co-operation with other coyotes. The pack, with up to 8 members, is a family affair. Youngsters that have not dispersed remain to help their parents. The hunt is not so organised as that of the wolf; a coyote pack relies more on

The coyote was long considered a solitary animal, but now we know that individuals sometimes live and hunt together. Prey mostly includes ground squirrels, rabbits and mice, although larger animals, such as pronghorn antelope and mountain sheep, are chased and caught by a hunting pack.

weight of numbers to harass and pull down large prey.

But having acquired food, it is another thing to keep it. Neighbouring groups respond to the staccato-like yelps and come to investigate. A large pack is at a distinct advantage. A pack avoids the humiliation of losing a dead elk to a rival gang with the help of group defence. A pack of 3-4 coyotes will successfully retain its stash, but a pair of animals is likely to lose its food to intruders.

ONE WHO PERFORMS MENIAL TASKS

JACKALS ARE MORE usually recognised as scavengers, often appearing at lion or hyena kills, spooking vultures and running away with whatever they can steal. But the jackal - and there are four species: golden, silverbacked, simien and sidestriped - depends less on carrion than one might imagine. Like many other predators, jackals are opportunists and will consume anything from fruit to frogs, and mice to gazelles. Where game is plentiful, scavenging provides a very small part of the diet. Hunting is usually co-operative, the pack consisting of an adult pair and yearlings staying with the family as 'helpers'.

Golden jackals chase Thompson's gazelles and they are about the right size for jackals to overpower. A solitary jackal does not do too well, succeeding in only 16 per cent of attacks.

BEWARE OF THE DOGS

SINCE WORLD WAR II, hunters and farmers with increasingly sophisticated weaponry have reduced Italy's wolf population to about 100 individuals. Most of the remaining animals live in small groups not far from Rome in the Abruzzo National Park, but despite their legal protection their future survival is threatened not directly by the activities of man, but by an animal that has taken over their place in the mountains - the feral dog.

Feral dogs are domestic dogs that have escaped or have been left to fend for themselves. They live in the wild, scavenging on scraps of food found at waste dumps or from garbage cans. Some have grouped together into loose gangs and are reverting to the pack behaviour of their ancient ancestor, the wolf.

One of the main problems is that there are so many. At the last count, there were an estimated 80,000 feral dogs, not including urban strays. And they can be dangerous, for many of the wild dogs are large, such as German shepherds and Pyrenean mountain dogs. Sheep are definitely at risk, but so are larger animals, including man. One field biologist studying the behaviour of feral dogs was tracked and chased. He was in no doubt what would have happened if he had not reached his car in time.

Near Rome, one group of dogs specialises in taking horses. In the wild, a pack of dogs would be unable to catch and bring down a free-running horse, but those fenced in a field are easy to panic and overpower.

Hunting is supplemented by scavenging. Those dogs taking livestock tend to live in remote and sparsely populated areas of the Appenines, the hill and mountain country normally inhabited by wolves. Natural prey, such as deer, has been exterminated, so both dogs and wolves come down to the valleys where people are living and turn to garbage for their daily food. Many villages have open garbage tips and the feral dogs take full advantage.

In the main, the pack dogs that behave like wolves live in the mountains, and the loners that behave like foxes live in the valleys. Solitary dogs are most likely new arrivals without a pack, and several might amicably share a home range -

Packs of feral dogs are beginning to appear in many parts of the world and have become established in Italy, Australia and Thailand. Much of their food is obtained by scavenging at rubbish dumps, but some better organised groups have taken to hunting cattle, sheep and horses, much as their wild wolf ancestors would have done.

perhaps the first step towards pack formation. Intruders are not made welcome and dogs from other parts of the valley are aggressively chased away. A new arrival, unaware of the boundaries, can overstep the mark and might be killed by the residents.

Unlike wolves, feral dogs do not have a strict pecking order. There is no alpha male and female. Any of the males and females mate and reproduce. A pack can enlarge rapidly. With so many dogs and so few wolves, livestock killings are more likely to be the action of dog packs rather than wolf packs. But it is the wolf that still retains its evil reputation and the wolf is blamed for the attacks.

In Australia, they have seen it all before. They too have a feral dog problem.

The dingos of Australia hunt alone when tackling small items of prey, such as marsupials, lizards and birds, but come together in packs to tackle kangaroos and wallabies. They communicate in howls for they are unable to bark. Pups learn to catch prey by watching their parents, and they are gradually allowed to take part in the hunt.

In ancient times, the only major killers were marsupial predators, such as the Tasmanian wolf, giant monitor lizards and eagles. But 20,000 years ago, the Aborigines colonised Australia and some of the late arrivals brought dogs, most likely descendants of the Indian wolf. Some escaped and took to living in the wild, and during the past 8,000 years the dingo has emerged as an effective co-operative predator that has upset irrevocably the ecology of the entire island continent of Australia.

A dingo is able to catch for itself a rabbit, grasshoppers and lizards, but a gang of dingos can tackle large, red or grey kangaroos and feral pigs. They cause havoc on sheep ranches and have even been known to kill people. A bounty has been placed on every dingo head.

HIGH-FLYING HIJACK

ELEONORA'S FALCONS VISIT the Mediterranean in summer. They breed, not in the spring as other birds, but in the autumn when the chicks of all the other birds have fledged and flown. They wait for the seasonal abundance of prey during the autumn migration. It is at this time that the young, inexperienced fledglings from northern Europe make their way south, and at key crossing sites along the Mediterranean coast the falcons are waiting.

Groups of falcons hold station at heights from near ground level to more than 3,000ft (1,000m). They simply hover and wait, a giant vertical gauntlet through which the migrants must pass. The falcons stoop on their prey, surprising it from above and behind. Some birds work together and engage in prolonged chases that exhaust their quarry and gain a meal for the waiting falcon chick. Only a small percentage of attacks is successful; nevertheless, one in 600 of the millions of birds on passage fall prey to the waiting raptors.

Lanner falcons frequent sea-cliffs and a pair of mated birds often patrol their patch, hunting together. The larger female flies in and out of the gullies, flushing jackdaws and pigeons away from the cliff-side. Waiting high on the wind is the male. He swoops in and intercepts the escaping birds.

FEATHERED FISHERMEN

BLUE-EYED SHAGS form fishing gangs. The birds do not co-operate like lions or wolves, but they do depend on each other to exploit their food source. They live around the cold, but nutrient-rich Southern Ocean and prey principally on

Blue-eyed shags (imperial shags) form huge rafts of birds on the sea's surface and feed together. They live on the southern shores of South America, near sub-Antarctic islands and along the coast of the Antarctic Peninsula, and form huge rafts mainly during the austral winter.

surface-living fish. The birds form enormous rafts on the sea's surface and float about waiting for a shoal to pass beneath. Every so often a bird dips its head under the water and scans the murky depths. As soon as prey is located, the spotter dives below and the rest of the flock follows. Confusion reigns. The fish swim rapidly in all directions. They may jig to avoid one cormorant only to meet the bill of another. There is little chance of escape. By hunting in a gang these birds maximise their chances, not only of locating food but also of catching it.

Seabirds, in general, tend to form loose gangs, by the very nature of nesting together. Huge numbers of birds pack shoulder to shoulder on cliff ledges and islands to form huge seabird cities, and there is some evidence to suggest that there is an element of co-operation, albeit unintentional, in the way they find food. The seabird colony, in effect, is an information centre. Birds are constantly flying to and fro, eager to catch food for their growing youngsters. An individual only has to watch returning birds with full crops and note the direction from which they came to know which way it should head out in order to find the fish or squid shoals.

Pelicans go even further and actively co-operate to consolidate the food supply. They swim along the surface, in an open horseshoe-shape, constantly dipping their enormous beaks below the water. In this way, they drive a shoal of fish into a corner and then scoop them up at leisure.

GENTLE GIANTS AND BUBBLE BLOWERS

ONE OF NATURE'S most impressive sights must be humpback whales feeding together. In the nutrient-rich, sub-polar and polar waters they co-operate in order to maximise their intake of food. Humpbacks need a lot of food. They must fatten up for the winter months, when they set out on vast journeys to and from their breeding grounds. Throughout most of the excursion, which may last for about two-thirds of the year and includes the rigours of courtship, mating and calving, they fast. Feeding, then, is at a premium during the brief Arctic or Antarctic summer. The prey consists of small fish, such as capelin, and krill, which are small, shrimp-like crustaceans. There are two main methods of collecting it - lunge-feeding and bubble-netting.

Lunging can be vertical or at an angle. Whales dive below a school of small fish and shoot rapidly upwards with mouths agape. The surface boils with a hissing sound, disturbed water caused by escaping prey. Momentarily all is quiet and then, with an almighty explosive roar, the whales burst through the surface, their heads emerging together, mouths wide open and throats distended with a churning soup of water and fish. Slowly, they sink back into the water, tongues pressed firmly against the roof of the mouth, the water squeezed between the rod-like baleen plates that trap the prey inside. In one gulp the concentrated puree is swallowed.

Usually a maximum of 7 whales lunge together, and they swim so closely that they are all touching when they erupt in a flailing, flower-like posy of flippers, flukes and baleen in a 50ft (15m) diameter circle at the surface.

The lunge can also be at an angle or horizontally across the sea's surface. Horizontal lunges might be performed while the whale is swimming upside down, or on its side with one flipper for a pennant sticking upright in the water.

Up to 40 whales might come together to feed. They break up into small groups, lunging in line-abreast - a behaviour known as echelon feeding - and exploiting patches of fish or plankton. The groups are usually transient, but several individuals, identified by the black-and-white marking on their tail flukes, have been seen to fish together in this co-operative way for several seasons in Glacier Bay, Alaska. Another aberrant fisher feeding off the Massachusetts coast has its own unique technique. It rises out of the water with its mouth closed and then sinks back down again with it partly open, creating a vortex into which the fish are drawn, much like the spout of water going out of a bathtub.

Humpback whales also blow bubbles, not for aggressive display - blowing bubbles is a way in which one humpback tells another humpback to push off - but to catch food. The technique is to blow a net of bubbles.

A submerged whale manoeuvres itself below a large shoal of small fish, such as herring or capelin, and begins to blow a circle of bubbles. As the bubbles rise, they form a hollow cylinder in the water column. The cylinder has the texture of a bubble net or curtain and it traps the shoal of fish inside. It is thought that they are frightened by the flashing reflections of the bubbles and they congregate into a tightening mass in the centre of the column. The whale, meanwhile, rises up through the centre of the column with its mouth open. The fish try to escape upwards, but are trapped by the surface. The whale bursts through the surface, its throat distended with water and frightened fish, and closes its gigantic mouth. The water is squeezed out through the baleen plates leaving the food behind.

Some gangs of whales are loyal to their group and tend to use the same feeding method regularly. Practice makes perfect, and well-drilled teams make effective predators.

UNDERWATER GANGS

STORIES OF SHOALS of predatory piranha attacking and devouring large animals in Amazonian rivers are legendary. Many fish have deadly teeth, but those of the piranha have become the stuff of nightmares. Of the twenty or more species, four are recognised as notorious killers. They have a mouth filled with razor-sharp, triangular teeth designed to slice off bite-sized pieces of flesh. A shoal, which can number hundreds if not thousands of individuals, can reduce a large capybara to a skeleton in less than 2 minutes. The fish pick the bones clean. There is a classic description of a piranha attack by William Innes, the doyen of home aquarium keepers. He wrote of a pig being dipped into a piranha-infested river and 'Each time it was lifted out of the water, it was reduced in size.'

Blood in the water is said to whip a shoal of piranhas into a demonic feeding frenzy, and although the smell of blood or body fluids makes them more likely to bite, it is the sight of the prey that triggers the attack. Piranhas only attack fish which are four times as long as they are wide. Fortunately for their shoal-mates, piranhas themselves are less than three times as long as they are wide.

Vying with the piranha for the title of 'world's most ferocious living fish' must be the blue fish of the Atlantic coast of the USA. It has been described as the ultimate 'animated chopping machine'. A shoal, working together, will tear into their prey, often fish little smaller than themselves, leaving a trail of blood, flesh fragments and pieces of entrails in their wake.

In the deep sea, small, 1-2ft-long dogfish form into roaming underwater packs. Luminous light-emitting organs along the body enable pack members to keep together in the dark of the abyss. They hunt together taking squid larger than themselves. Like angry wasps, it is thought that they swarm all over the prey, anchoring themselves with their pointed top row of teeth and slicing off chunks of flesh with the razor-sharp lower band of teeth.

But perhaps the most appealing story of undersea co-operation comes from Australia. There, on the coral reefs of the Great Barrier Reef, a small, brightly coloured, petal-like, pink, white and blue gnathopyllid shrimp attacks starfish, including the infamous crown-of-thorns which is out of control and gobbling huge sections of the vulnerable reef system. Male-female pairs of shrimps work together and tickle the starfish's feet, which causes the spiny star to loosen its hold on the coral. Gradually, they turn it over. Once it is upside down, the shrimps feast on the soft underside before the unfortunate starfish can right itself.

PACKS OF SPIDERS

MOST SPIDERS AVOID meeting other spiders and only do so when absolutely necessary, such as at mating time. Even then they are very careful not to upset the spouse or they might end up as dinner. But in tropical parts some web spiders co-operate.

In Panama, one species of theridiid spider lives in enormous colonies containing up to 10,000 individuals. They live on sheet-like webs as large as 12ft (4m) across and trap insects. When prey collides with the web, the vibrations of its struggles attract the attention of the closest spiders. If it is too large and too difficult for them to subdue, more and more spiders pile in to help. The co-operation means that these small spiders, just $^{1}/_{4}$in (5mm) long, can tackle prey over $2^{1}/_{2}$in (6cm) long and provide more than enough food for themselves and the rest of the colony.

These social spiders live together in the Okavango Delta region of northern Botswana. They are one of 30 species which have taken to overpowering large prey co-operatively. The greater 'silk spinning power' of many spiders means the group can spin a larger web with greater catching potential. As a group they can also chase off dangerous wasps and bees.

A troop of olive or 'common' baboons in Kenya indulges in a session of mutual grooming. The activity is often directed towards high-ranking members or 'favoured' individuals, such as a mother with baby, and it promotes alliances within the troop. A troop that grooms together, fights together.

The yawn of an olive baboon gives a clear message that the owner is not to be trifled with; it also reveals the enormous canine teeth with which a large, male baboon can despatch a small antelope.

Baboons sometimes form loose hunting gangs and catch gazelle, domestic livestock and young animals hiding in the grass. Co-operation, however, stops at the kill, for this male will not share any of the Thompson's gazelle fawn he has caught with any others in the troop.

Golden jackals are more successful at hunting prey, such as Thompson's gazelle fawns if there are two or more jackals in the hunt. A pair can better outwit a gazelle mother who is more than capable of chasing away a lone jackal. One distracts the mother while the other grabs the fawn. The prey is killed with bites to the groin and belly.

◀

Black-backed jackals scavenge a small carcass. They must be quick to eat for other scavengers are probably waiting in the wings to steal the food away.

▲

Pairs of lanner falcons hunt together. They live in southern Europe and North Africa, often patrolling cliffs in lands and deserts bordering the Mediterranean. Prey includes birds up to the size of pigeons and jackdaws, which are surprised in the air, and sand grouse, rats, rabbits, lizards and grasshoppers, which are caught on the ground.

▼

White pelicans swim in line abreast, herding fish before them. As one, the birds dip their enormous bills below the surface and scoop up the concentrated shoals of fish.

Each autumn Eleonora's falcons wait at crossing points along the Mediterranean and pursue young migrants on their first journey south. The small birds are caught in the talons whilst on the wing. Two or more falcons might co-operate to bring down prey.

▷

The gape of the piranha, the legendary killer fish of the Amazon, is all that it promises to be. The razor-sharp teeth can strip the flesh off prey in seconds. Piranha feed together, shoals exceeding 100 or in some places 1,000 individuals.

▽

The smaller species of barracuda swim and hunt in shoals. They are formidable predators with large, pointed jaws armed with pin-sharp teeth. They are capable of fast swimming and they herd other fish together to make catching easier.

Humpback whales head for the nutrient-rich polar waters in summer to feed on fish and krill. Sometimes, whales form summertime alliances and lunge together in a line at the surface, scooping shoals of fish, such as capelin, into their enormous maws.

Weapons, Lures & Traps

4

Specialist hunting strategies sometimes demand particular adaptations of the body, including specialised structures to entice a foolhardy victim within range of a fearsome mouth or to ensnare, trap or impale prey before it has time to escape. In the natural world, there are anglers, mimics, flashers, winklers, probers, smashers and strikers - a galaxy of animals kitted out with an arsenal of weapons to gain a meal.

Many animals have developed the jaws for seizing prey - some with teeth inside the mouth and others, like birds, with beaks outside. Some predators have highly adapted fore or hind limbs with spiky outgrowths and claws for grabbing and holding. Some, like the pygmy owl, use one or the other depending on the prey - small birds are grasped and killed in the talons, while mice are dispatched by repeated pecks at the head. And what nature could not provide naturally, animals have acquired for themselves. Some have developed that ability so long thought to be the preserve of humans - the use of tools. A few even make their own.

Having caught their prey, very few hunting animals chew their meal. By bolting the food, a large amount can be swallowed quickly, a behaviour which prevents others stealing the meat and which enables the hunter to take advantage of a sudden glut of food. Some animals, like snakes, take a while to swallow their often very large prey. They must dislocate the jaws in order for it to pass through the mouth, but having ingested such an enormous meal, they will have no need to eat for some time to come.

SAWS AND SPEARS

THE MOST IMPRESSIVE undersea weapon must be from the world of fishes: it is the long, slightly flattened, rapier-like sword of the swordfish, and its billfish look-alikes - the sail fish, spearfish and marlins. The sword is a long, bony projection of the upper jaw covered with tiny spiky denticles like those found on shark skin. The way these fish use their swords is not clear, but it is thought that they

A sailfish, with its dorsal fin raised in a threat display, scours Mexico's Sea of Cortez for food. Some biologists consider it to be the fastest fish in the sea, with speeds up to 67mph (109km/h) recorded. When travelling at speed, the large dorsal fin rests in a slot on the back, and the other fins are pressed tight against the body.

U S E F U L   W E A P O N S

Many animal weapons are developed by the male of a species for fighting with other males of the same species, and the cause of all such scraps is the defence of territory or the right to mate. Some of these weapons, however, can be used to obtain food. The enormous tusks of a bull walrus are grown to impress other walruses, but they are also good for digging up clams from the sea-floor. Most of the time the walrus pushes its upper lip through the bottom sediments, much like a pig routing for truffles. It is also able to blow jets of water into the mud in order to excavate a mollusc that is particularly difficult to extract. And if that fails, it can always use the tusks for a bit of extra leverage. Likewise, the long, canine teeth of a dominant male baboon are displayed with a yawn to indicate his status, but they can also be used to quickly dispatch a young impala or hare that the monkey has found hiding in the grass. And the extraordinary elongated tooth of the narwhal is used in male-versus-male 'sword fights', but it could also play a role in echolocating for fish. Strong vibrations run down the tooth when the narwhal vocalises. Might the tooth serve to focus sounds?

rush into shoals of surface-swimming fish swiping at them with lateral movements of the sword. The stunned and mutilated prey are picked up after the attack.

The sawfish, though resembling the swordfish and billfishes, is more closely related to the rays. It has a flattened saw with 16-32 widely spaced, very sharp, teeth-like projections along each side of the blade. The teeth are modified dermal denticles (the tiny, teeth-like projections that cover the skin of sharks and rays). The tough sword is made of cartilage, but is calcified to add strength. In large specimens, such as the southern sawfish of the Atlantic, the saw can be up to 6ft long and 1ft wide at the point it leaves the head. The fish itself can be up to 20ft long, and one specimen caught in the West Indies had an estimated weight of 5,300lbs. The Australian green sawfish grows even bigger with lengths of 24ft recorded. And a 46ft monster was reputed to have entered the Chao Phya River in Thailand.

In the open sea, the sawfish attacks a shoal of fish making powerful side-to-side thrashing movements with the saw and leaving a trail of dead and dying bodies in its wake. At leisure it returns to gather up the casualties.

In shallow waters, it tends to feed on the bottom, gathering bottom-dwelling prey into its mouth, which is slung under the head, aft of the saw. It might use the tip of the saw to weedle out shellfish and molluscs from the sea-floor, and many sawfish are seen with saws that have the tips worn down. It has also been seen to spike a surface-swimmer on its teeth, take the victim to the seabed, scrape it from the saw and eat it.

It has been known to attack man, although these may have been accidents. There are reports from Panama Bay of people being killed by sawfish and a story from India of a bather being sliced in half.

IT'S A KNOCKOUT

ANOTHER EXTRAORDINARY UNDERWATER weapon system has been developed by a colourful collection of creatures known as stomatopods or mantid shrimps. These tropical crustaceans are shrimp-like but not true shrimps. They have eight pairs of appendages of which the last three are used for walking and the first five for feeding, digging and cleaning.

The mantid shrimp has an incredible pair of eyes. They are large and swivel independently like those of the chameleon, and they are kept clean by brushes on the first pair of appendages. The third, fourth and fifth pairs have hooks for manipulating prey and other objects, but the most interesting appendages are the second pair. These are larger than the others and have evolved into powerful weapons. And their shape indicates the type of prey the shrimp might catch.

There are stomatopods which have a modified appendage tipped with a multi-pronged spear. They specialise in spiking soft-bodied animals, such as shrimps and fish. If prey comes close to the mantid shrimp, the appendage unfolds, the spear is unleashed and the victim is impaled on the spikes. It is drawn to the mouth and dissected by the other mouth appendages and the cutting jaws.

The second group contains the smashers. Instead of a spear, they have a large, hammer-like heel. These characters are capable of tackling tough, armoured animals, such as crabs, hermit crabs and sea-snails. Crabs are first incapacitated by having their limbs knocked off. Then, a rain of continuous

Mantis shrimps are like ancient knights in armour. They have a tough exoskeleton and some expand their tail to form an armoured shield. Some are equipped with spears, others with hammer-like clubs. This individual has harpooned a fish.

blows against the carapace breaks the victim apart in order that the aggressive mantid shrimp can get at the softer parts inside. The hammer is so powerful that a mantid shrimp is able to smash its way out of a glass aquarium tank.

TOOL USERS

IN THE GALAPAGOS ISLANDS, off the coast of Ecuador in the Pacific Ocean, there are no woodpeckers, but there is another bird which has taken over the vacant niche - the woodpecker finch. Being a finch and only recently (in geological terms) having found its food source, it does not have the anatomical where-withal to exploit it. Woodpeckers have long, powerful beaks with which they can hammer into wood and a specialised tongue to dislodge wood-boring grubs. The woodpecker finch has neither. Instead, it makes a tool to do the job. It first

The comical and cuddly sea-otter is a tool-user. After diving down to the seabed, it has brought up a clam and is breaking it open against a rock 'anvil' that rests on its stomach. Sea-otters live amongst the kelp forests around north Pacific coasts.

visits a cactus plant and breaks off a spine. Then, it takes the spine to a crack or crevice in which an insect is confined and uses it to winkle out the food.

Chimpanzees do the same with termites. They find suitable grass stems and poke them down the entrance tunnels of termite nests. The soldier termites attack the twig, those with large jaws fastening themselves on to the 'intruder'. The chimp pulls the twig plus termites out of the hole and either licks them off or wipes them off with its hand. The choice of stem is carefully considered, and if it is bent during the 'fishing' process, the damaged part is bitten off or the stem discarded. Chimps also use small sticks to probe for ants, bees and honey, and they break open ant nests with larger branches. It is thought that young chimps learn the technique from their parents and then refine it by experience.

Other primates also use tools. Capuchin monkeys use twigs to dig for insects in the bark of trees, and baboons use sticks to probe for insects. They have also been known to smash a scorpion with a rock.

One of the most charming tool users must be the sea-otter from the Pacific coast of North America. These true marine mammals dive to the bottom of the shallow sea and bring up crabs, sea-urchins, clams, mussels and a stone on which to break open the prey. They feed whilst floating on their backs. The 4in (10cm) diameter stone is placed on the chest, like an anvil. The prey is held in the front paws and banged repeatedly against the stone. Otters have been known to keep a 'favourite' stone for several feeding expeditions, holding it under the armpit during the dive. Like the chimps, young otters are thought to learn their skills from the parent.

KILLING FEET

FEET CAN BE KILLERS. Birds of prey have deadly feet. They catch and kill their prey, not in the bill, but with powerful, clawed toes or talons. The feet can accommodate to different size prey - overlapping talons crushing a small animal, and a spreading foot grasping large prey. In some cases the foot has become so specialised that the hunter is limited to the animals it can take.

Sea-eagles, fish eagles and ospreys have rough spicules on the bottom of their toes to help keep a hold of slippery fish. Snake eagles have stout legs and short toes adapted for catching slim, writhing snakes. They break the snake's vulnerable backbone on first impact.

Large eagles, like the golden and Verreaux's eagles, have large, strong feet with a long, hind toe and sharp talon, an adaptation for grabbing and killing large mammals such as hares and hyrax. Verreaux's eagles feed almost exclusively on hyrax, which they pluck from cliff-sides or treetops while the unfortunate victims are sunbathing. The grasp is so strong it is said that a person would be unable to loosen the grip of even a single toe.

The harpy eagle has the most powerful raptorial feet. The adult female bird has an ankle 1in (2cm) thick, to which is attached a foot spanning 9-10in (23-25cm). Each toe is tipped with dagger-like talons more than $1^1/_2$in (38mm) long. With such a weapon, the harpy is capable of catching and dispatching large mammals, such as pigs and antelope, and can kill a small, frail-bodied monkey with one squeeze.

One bird of prey, the secretary bird, does not have the same grasping claws of its relatives for it spends most of its time on the ground. It requires legs and feet for walking rather than catching. It does, however, occasionally kill with its feet. Forsaking its normal prey of insects and rodents which it picks off with its beak, the bird tackles larger objects, such as snakes, by stamping on them.

The cat family also has killer claws, but unlike those of the eagle, they are retractable. The claws themselves tend to be large, curved and sharp, like scimitars, and they enable the cat to grab and hold on to prey. At rest, each claw is retracted inside a fleshy sheath in the paw. This protects the tip and ensures that it remains sharp. At the moment of prey capture, muscles protract the claws and they are ready for action. A cat's paws are also adapted for a stealthy approach with soft pads on the underside. The cheetah has harder pads with a tyre-like tread for grip and semi-retractable claws that it uses like spiked running shoes.

Of the invertebrates, the starfish have interesting feet. They have tube feet, and there are lots of them. Along the underside of each starfish arm there are rows of tube feet, each connected to its neighbour by a water-filled tube. Water is pumped in and out of the feet to make them work, and on its end each foot is flattened to form a sucker. The starfish is able to progress slowly across the seabed or rock face using its hundreds of sucker feet, but the system comes into its own when it stumbles upon its prey.

The retractable, needle-sharp claws of a young mountain lion not only help it grip the bough of a tree as it climbs down, but also assist the animal to grab and hold on to struggling prey. They fold back into slots when not in use and, therefore, remain sharp and ready for instant action.

The soft pads on a leopard's foot allow the animal to approach its victim unheard. It must place its foot on the ground in such a way so as to prevent a 'chattering' effect of the elasticated pad covering.

This brown pelican in the Everglades, Florida, has one of the most specialised and exaggerated bills in the bird world. Brown pelicans dive for fish, often from a great height. The long bill and sagging throat pouch can accommodate fish up to 1ft long.

Starfish, being slow, tend to be successful in hunting bivalved shellfish. Many, like mussels and clams, are unable to escape, whilst scallops are able to clap their shells together and take off under jet propulsion. The only defence put up by a mussel, though, is to pull its two shells tightly shut and wait for the danger to pass. The starfish has a way to get around that. It straddles the shellfish, clamping its rows of suckers on to both shells. Suction is aided by a secretion on the suction pads, and the starfish is able to pull the shells apart. As long as there is a small gap, it can evert its thin-walled stomach from the mouth in the middle of the central disc of its body and push it inside the shell, where it digests the mussel in situ.

TEETH, BEAKS AND RASPS

MOUTH PARTS ARE ALL-IMPORTANT for either catching food or dealing with it before swallowing. Birds have bills with no teeth; mammals, reptiles and fish have mouths armed with teeth; and armoured animals like insects and crustaceans have appendages modified as scissors.

Birds' bills come in all shapes and sizes, each one adapted for a particular way of life. Birds of prey have strong, hooked bills for tearing at flesh; herons have long, sharp bills for stabbing and seizing fish; pelicans have large, wide bills with a pouch slung below to retain the fish they have caught; many waders have long, slender bills for probing sand and mud; avocets have upturned bills with which they scythe through the water and trap small marine animals; spoonbills have 'spoons' with which they can extract invertebrates from the mud; and puffins have a peculiarly colourful, blunt bill in which they can carry several sand-eels, hanging sideways across the beak, at any one time.

Although birds do not have teeth as such, the merganser has a serrated, tooth-like edge to the upper and lower parts of the bill with which it can grab and hold on to slithery fish. And the anhinga - of the darter family from Central and South America - has special tendons in its long, thin neck with which it can rapidly straighten the neck and impale a fish on its very sharp, pointed bill.

Big and small cats, and wild dogs and wolves have large, pointed, canine teeth. With these, they are able to grasp the throat of a victim and hold on tight until it suffocates. The back teeth are designed for slicing and tearing flesh.

Snakes have backward-pointing teeth which prevent prey from wriggling free and, with specialised jaw movements, help manoeuvre it back into the throat.

In the sea, the teeth of sharks have contributed much in sustaining their reputation as nature's ultimate killers, but not all sharks have the same sort of teeth. There are large teeth and small teeth, sharp and blunt teeth, saw-like and knife-like teeth, grasping and holding teeth, and grinding and cutting teeth; but above all, sharks' teeth are endlessly replaceable. They are on a kind of conveyor-belt, with the newly developing teeth at the back and the completed teeth at the front. As the teeth are lost - at a rate of a row in 8 days for the lemon shark - the developing teeth move forward to replace them. In this way a shark is always ready for action. Like many other predators, though, it cannot chew, and in order to take a chunk out of a large victim it must shake its head vigorously until the teeth have sliced through flesh and bone.

Mako and sand tiger sharks have long, pointed, awl-like teeth for grasping fish and squid. Great whites have serrated, triangular-shaped, saw-like teeth for hacking through mammalian flesh and blubber. Tiger sharks have characteristic L-shaped, serrated teeth with which they can cut through turtle shells. Dogfish have blunt teeth for crushing mollusc shells, and horned sharks have two types of teeth - small, sharp ones at the front of the mouth for catching small fish and flat, tile-like crushing teeth at the back of the mouth to deal with shellfish. The tiny 17in (42cm) long, large-toothed, cookie-cutter shark, which takes circular chunks of flesh from the bodies of squid, has the largest teeth for its body size of any known shark. The relatively enormous, triangular-cusped teeth are 25 per cent of the head length.

The most curious teeth in the animal world, perhaps, are those of certain molluscs, for the teeth or denticles are on the ribbon-like 'tongue' or radulla. The dog whelk, so common on British shores, uses its radulla to prize apart the upper plates which protect the barnacle from drying out and to bore into the shell's mussels. Small, round holes in a mussel shell are witness to dog whelk predation. After boring the hole, the radulla acts as a conveyor-belt to extract the tissue. Necklace shells soften the shell of the prey with acid before boring a hole, and cone shells go one better. Having trapped its prey, maybe a fish in a crevice, the cone shell harpoons it with one of the teeth at the end of the radulla and injects a nerve poison that paralyses the prey. The poison is so powerful it is dangerous to man.

DEATH BY POISON

THERE ARE MORE human deaths from bee, wasp and scorpion stings, and spider and snake bites, than there are, say, from attacks by monstrous sharks.

Scorpions are probably the most ancient stinging things. They have been around for at least 400 million years. They use their sting mostly for defence, but faced with a violently struggling prey the scorpion will use its venom. The sting is carried arched over the body at the tip of the curved abdomen. Prey is caught in the crab-like claws, and if large or out of control, it is stung. Some, but not all, scorpions are dangerous to man. The deadly ones produce a toxin which attacks the nerves, causing partial paralyses and fever, and sometimes death.

Insect stings are dangerous, not to a healthy adult person but to those suffering a weak heart or strong, allergic reaction. To prey animals, an insect sting is always deadly, and some stinging insects have the capacity to inflict lasting damage.

Parasitic wasps, like the digger-wasps of Arizona, are dangerous to large spiders. In a seemingly one-sided struggle, the small but agile wasp is able to out-manoeuvre and overpower the large, hairy tarantula spider. The wasp avoids the spider's formidable, poisonous fangs and stabs it with its sting. The spider is not killed but paralysed. It becomes a living food store for the wasp's offspring. She lays her eggs inside the spider and when they hatch they eat the spider's body from the inside out.

But spiders themselves have dangerous venoms. The most dangerous to man is the notorious black widow spider, which accounted for 55 deaths in the USA before an antivenom was developed. The spider does not deliberately bite

The black widow spider, recognised by its shiny black body and bright-red, hour-glass marking, is the most dangerous to people. The female has a bite which is excruciatingly painful, but rarely fatal. It will attack anything that causes vibrations in its web, and is a common inhabitant of outside toilets in tropical countries.

people; it is the only way it knows of defending itself, but in its more natural encounters the spider purposely subdues or kills its prey with poison. A spider stabs at its victim with a pair of large, sharp, hollow fangs. Having incapacitated its victim, it does not slice up the body and swallow it; rather it pierces the skin and sucks out the body fluids.

Centipedes also have a poisonous bite. Hollow, fang-like claws at the front end are fed by ducts from special venom glands. The victim is grasped, injected and paralysed, and then sliced up by the jaws. Large species have enormous fangs and will lie in wait below stones and undergrowth for lizards, frogs, toads and even mice. The larger tropical species have a painful bite that can be dangerous to man.

Two species of lizard - the gila monster of Arizona and the beaded lizard of Mexico's Sonoran Desert - have venom glands in the lower jaw. The glands consist of three or four lobes each with a duct running to the base of the large teeth, which have grooves along which the poison can flow.

Snakes have paired fangs in the upper jaw with which they deliver their venom. Some snakes have the fangs at the back of the mouth and they tend to chew on a victim in order to inject the venom. The venom is produced by modified salivary glands and is delivered along a groove in the fangs. Other snakes have large, hollow, tubular fangs at the front of the upper jaw. Cobras and mambas have fangs which are permanently erect and ready for stabbing a victim, whereas rattlesnakes and vipers have their fangs folded back into the roof of the mouth when resting and only bring them out at the moment of biting.

The most formidable poisonous serpent in the world must be the king cobra, which can reach 6m in length. It feeds mainly on other snakes, but has been known to attack and kill an elephant in self-defence. One of the most deadly venomous snakes to man is considered to be the taipan of Australia. This 3m-long brown snake, the longest of Australia's poisonous snakes, manufactures huge volumes of highly toxic venom. An individual was once 'milked' and delivered a cupful of poison, enough to kill tens of thousands of mice. The fangs are longer than in most snakes, and so the taipan can inject its lethal brew deep into the body of its victim. Instead of a single strike and grasp, the snake strikes repeatedly at the prey. Death for the unfortunate small mammal or bird is instantaneous.

One curious and rare small mammal has a poisonous bite. It is the squirrel-sized, shrew-like solendon of the West Indies. There are two species - the agouti of Haiti and almiqui of Cuba - and both have a long, trunk-like snout. The poison is in the saliva. Shrews have a similar toxic saliva.

GONE FISHING

THE MOST WELL-KNOWN lure in the animal kingdom must be that used by the angler fish. There are many species, some in coastal waters and others in the deep sea (see below). Most familiar is the 'monk-fish', with its enormous, cavernous mouth. It lies very still on a sandy or muddy seabed, feathery outgrowths enabling it to blend in with its background. But on the front of its head the first dorsal spine stands alone and has a fleshy tip. The fish can move the spine in such a way that the tip resembles a small, animate object worthy of investigation by a fish looking for a meal. As soon as the prey is within a few inches of the angler's snout, the mouth opens wide, the fish swallows violently and the prey is drawn in with the inrush of water. It all happens in an instant, backpointing teeth preventing the prey from escaping. Atlantic anglers can grow to 5.6ft (1.7m) long and weigh up to 88lb (40kg), the accompanying mouth capable of taking conger eels, gurnards, rays and even diving birds. One greedy angler was once found dead having choked on a gull.

In the tropics the colourful frogfishes are relatives of the anglers and they adopt a similar strategy to fool prey. The lures often resemble a white or pink wriggling worm that coils and uncoils like a worm out of its burrow.

Siphonophores are free-floating, colonial relatives of jellyfish. They might be considered as 'simple' animals, yet these tiny creatures show an amazingly sophisticated method of luring prey to their tentacles. Some species of siphono-phores are capable of movement and can wriggle themselves into the centre of dense patches of prey where they take pot-luck. Other slow-moving relatives allow nothing to chance. In one type, the sting cells with which they kill their prey are grouped together into red-coloured batteries of cells that have two sensitive hairs that trigger all the cells in the group. The battery of cells mimics the copepod (tiny crustaceans that live in the zooplankton) prey that they catch even to the point of pulsing like copepods. Another species has the sting cells shaped like tiny fish larvae, complete with eyes and fins. They trap the small sea creatures that prey on fish larvae using the battery of mimicking cells to entice them closer.

On a larger dimension, the alligator-snapping turtle also uses a lure. It lies partly buried in the mud of slow-moving rivers in the eastern and south-eastern

In the darkness of the oceanic abyss, the deep-sea angler fish attracts prey towards its ample mouth with an elongated first dorsal fin ray or illicium - the fishing line - which ends in a luminous, flashing, frilly 'esca' or bait. A branched appendage or barbel, which is faintly luminous, is slung under the lower jaw.

parts of North America. Only the head and open mouth protrudes from the river-bed. The sides, roof and floor of the mouth and most of the tongue are dark-coloured, but a small outgrowth on the tongue is conspicuous by its covering of red spots. The turtle can wriggle the outgrowth too, and to all intents and purposes it looks like a juice worm. Any small fish that comes to take the worm finds itself right in the turtle's mouth. All the predator need do is snap its jaws shut and the prey is trapped.

A similar ploy has been developed by certain snakes. The young of deadly poisonous snakes such as the fer-de-lance, water moccasin and copperhead have yellow tips to their tails. If it is wriggled in front of a frog or toad, the movement attracts the amphibian within striking distance of the snake.

The tiny nymph of the assassin bug of Costa Rica is a tool-maker. It has a penchant for termites and has found a way of fooling the normally aggressive

This assassin bug nymph from West Africa disguises itself with the skins of its victims and particles of sand. This enables it to approach its prey, protected by the prey's odour, and grab another without being detected and attacked.

termite soldiers so that it can prey on termite workers without coming to any harm. First, the nymph 'dresses up'. It places small pieces of the termite nest on its body, which gives it the 'scent' of the colony. Thus disguised, it sidles up to the entrance of the nest and grabs the next termite to emerge, injects digestive enzymes into it and sucks it dry. It then uses the dried-out shell as a lure to catch more termites. Since nothing is ever wasted in a termite colony, certainly not the protein-rich skin of a dead corpse, it too is snatched from under the very noses of the soldiers. The bug has been seen to 'angle' for termites in this way for up to 3 hours, in which time it caught as many as 30 - 1 termite every 6 minutes.

The green heron not only uses tools but makes them as well. In order to entice a fish from cover and up to the surface, the heron throws out baits, much as a fly-fisherman would do. They might be live baits, such as insects, or artificial lures fashioned from twigs, feathers or made from pieces of biscuit. If a twig is too long, the bird snaps it in two until it has sections of the correct length. These are scattered on the water and any fish that ventures into the open to eat the bait is grabbed instantly.

The black heron goes hunting with a sun visor. It darts about the shallows, stopping occasionally to peer into the water. As it does so, it fans open its wings and brings them up and over its head like a large, black, feathered parasol. It is thought that the wings shield the bird's eyes from the sun and cut down reflections from the surface of the water.

LIGHT LURES

GLOW-WORMS AND FIREFLIES are not worms or flies at all, but are beetle larvae. Their luminosity is primarily an aid to courtship, but for one species it is also a way of getting food. The female fireflies of one species mimics the luminous call-sign of another species. The males are attracted down by what they believe to be a female of their own species, but quickly discover that they have been enticed to their death.

In caves at Lamington National Park, Australia, a luminous curtain is created by the larvae of flies. The glow attracts prey, which is caught on the sticky threads dangling below the larvae that are attached to the cave roof.

In the Waitomo Caves in New Zealand luminous insects have become a tourist attraction and represent one of the great wonders of nature. Hanging from the roof of the caves are hundreds of glowing strands that form a bright, luminescent, bluish-green curtain. They are made by the larvae of a small fly and they are the way this enterprising insect catches its food.

Each larva, protected by a silken sheath, clings to the ceiling and exudes sticky threads that can be seen in the dark. Normally about 20 strands, varying from 6in to 2ft, are spun with some individuals dropping as many as 70 threads at any one time. Each strand has globules of mucous at 2in intervals. The luminous organ is in the larva's tail, and it shines down on the mucous, reflecting on the strands in such a way that they resemble glowing strings of pearls. Prey insects, attracted by the light, are caught and trapped on the strands and are reeled in like fish on fishing lines.

In the deeper parts of the sea, where light from the surface is barely visible or is absent altogether, light lures are common. The deep-sea angler fishes go one better than their shallow-water cousins by having a light organ on the tip of a modified first dorsal fin spine. The spine has become separated from the rest of the dorsal fin and moved to a position at the front of the fish's head. It is pivoted at its base on a miniature ball-and-socket joint that enables the lure to be waved about in any direction. The luminous tip may take the form of a simple swelling or is embellished with frills and filaments to make an appetising-looking bait. A patch of skin, without pigment, allows the bioluminescence to shine through. Tiny predators are enticed by the movements of the lure to within one-gulp-distance of the fish's mouth.

The light is not produced by the fish but by symbiotic bacteria that are cultured in special compartments within the lure. They are encouraged to glow when oxygenated blood is pumped into the chamber. When at rest, the fish shuts down its light organ simply by temporarily cutting off the blood supply.

The black angler fish, which lives at about 1,197ft (365m) at the bottom of the sea, has a luminous forked structure on the roof of its mouth. One species of hatchet fish probably attracts prey right into its mouth with the aid of two patches of luminescent tissue that can glow for 30 minutes at a time. And one species of lantern fish has light organs on its tongue.

The deep-sea, scaled dragon fishes have luminous chin barbels that are thought to attract prey to the mouth. One species sports a barbel ten times the length of its body with a tip that is luminous.

The mid-water viper fish behave in a similar way to angler fish. They have a modified second dorsal fin spine, tipped with a luminous lure, that has become even more elongated. The predator hangs motionless in the water, its head lower than its tail, with the fin-ray reaching over the head so that the lure dangles in front of the mouth. They look fearsome, with enormous mouths and gigantic teeth, but, fortunately, they are only 2-12in (5-30cm) long.

COME INTO MY PARLOUR

THE MOST WELL-KNOWN and perhaps the most beautiful of animal traps is the orb web constructed by certain spiders. Its design is remarkably precise and the materials with which it is made are amazingly strong. If pieces of man-made steel thread and spider silk of the same diameter were slowly loaded with increasing weight, the steel would snap first. Spider silk is five times stronger than steel. And not only that - spider silk stretches; it can stretch twice as far as the equivalent strand of nylon. It is also produced rapidly and in large quantities. In a laboratory test, a spider produced a half-a-mile of thread in 10 minutes. An average orb web is completed, wind and weather permitting, in about half an hour.

The web itself is suspended from a single, horizontal, bridge strand. Below this, a radiating pattern of threads joins from the points in the vegetation on the outside to a central hub at the centre of the web. Immediately outside the hub are the strengthening sections of closely spiralling threads, and outside this part is the catching zone, consisting of a spiral of sticky threads on which the prey is caught. The droplets of sticky material are produced from a special gland and daubed on to the threads at regular intervals.

The reflectivity of the sticky droplets is important. If they are too large andthere are too many, they will reflect too much light and flying insects are able to spot them and avoid the trap. The web must reflect as little light as possible, and the ideal droplet size, for a web in the open, is twice the diameter of the thread itself. Those spiders catching night-flying insects need be less diligent. In the dark, they are able to use large droplets and so are able to catch moths that would normally escape a modestly sticky, day-type web because they are able to shed wing scales and escape.

Spiders spinning very large webs, however, have a major problem. How do they stop large creatures, such as birds, from flying into and tearing the web? Somehow they must make their webs invisible to insects yet visible to birds. They do this by weaving in a thickened band of silk, called a stabilimenta, across the web. It is like a road sign that tells of an obstacle ahead. Birds flying towards an orb web have been seen to put their brakes on and fly over the top. By putting in the warning sign, the spider need not remake his web every day.

The net-throwing or ogre-faced spider anchors its web at the ends of its legs. By day, it stays hidden in a tree mimicking a twig, but by night it spins an A-shaped frame of silk from which it hangs, and constructs a net the size of a postage stamp which is attached to the feet of its front four legs. When ready to capture prey, it hangs upside down by its back four legs quite close to the ground. As an insect passes beneath, it lunges down and stretches the silken net over the victim, trapping it against the ground. A poisonous bite dispatches the prey and the spider sucks it dry.

The bolas spider has another strategy. It too hangs upside down, but only produces a single thread which dangles from the tip of one of its legs. At the other end of the line is a sticky globule, which releases a smell that resembles the sex pheromone of female moths. Male moths flying about in search of a female are attracted by the smell and blunder into the globule. The line stretches - up to six times its original length - to absorb the weight and energy of the struggling moth. The glue is so strong that scientists have thought it hard for man to reproduce. Once caught, the moth is hauled in and cocooned in silk. As many as eight moths may be snagged in a night, each one wrapped up and saved for later when the spider can eat it at its leisure.

TAKE AIM, FIRE

FEW ANIMALS ACTUALLY hurl projectiles at their prey, but one such hunter is the archer fish. It lives in fresh, salt and brackish waters, particularly in mangrove swamps, from India to northern Australia, and eats insects. The prey is usually sitting on an overhanging twig or leaf, and the fish spits at it to knock it down.

In order to be able to spit droplets of water to any distance, the fish has developed specialised features in its mouth. It has a groove in the roof of the mouth and the tongue is modified to press against the groove to form a 'tube', in effect the barrel of a water pistol. At the moment of discharge, the tongue is pressed to the roof of the mouth, the gills closed, and the front of the tongue flicks out the water droplets. A mature fish can knock down an insect which is up to 5ft (1.5m) above the water surface, and with a degree of accuracy.

The spitting spider, as its name suggests, also spits. In an eighth of a second, it spits a glob of sticky material a distance of 2cm sticking the prey to any convenient surface. Avoiding dangerous insects like wasps, bees and ants, the spitting spider prefers moths. It also has a penchant for other spiders. It spits at them and sticks them to their own webs.

Ant-lions throw stones, or, at least, particles of sand. They are the larvae of insects, known as 'doodle-bugs', that are closely related to lacewings and alder flies. They live in sandy places in the tropics or sub-tropics and they dig pits.

The pit is a conical-shaped depression which the insect carefully constructs. The ant-lion walks backwards in a circle, gradually spiralling inwards. It loads sand on to its head, and then throws it to one side or the other until the pit is

The Egyptian vulture is a deft stone-thrower. Faced with a large, tough ostrich egg, it takes to throwing rocks at it in order to break it open and get at the bonanza of nutritious yolk inside.

completed. Pits may be as large as 4in (10cm) in diameter and 20in (50cm) deep.

The ant-lion buries itself in the bottom of the pit, with just its enormous, pincer-like jaws protruding, and waits for a victim, like an ant or other small insect, to blunder in. The pit walls are very steep and so the prey finds it difficult to climb out. In addition, the walls are lined with fine sand, which is far less stable than coarse sand. If, however, the prey seems to be making good its escape, the ant-lion throws sand at it, knocking it back into the centre of the pit. There it can grasp the victim, pierce it and suck out the body fluids.

The most famous of the stone throwers, perhaps, is the Egyptian vulture. It throws rocks at ostrich eggs, but is not very accurate and needs many attempts before breaking them open. The habit seems to come from the vulture's innate tendency to throw eggs. The birds raid pelican and flamingo colonies for eggs

An ant-lion, lying in wait at the base of its specially constructed, sand-lined, pit-fall trap, grabs an ant with its powerful mandibles. The ant had stumbled into the pit and was unable to climb out.

which they can hurl down and break. Faced with an ostrich egg, they do the only thing that comes naturally and throw an egg-shaped (rather than a jagged) stone at it. The behaviour seems not to be learned, but is acquired simply by trial and error during the bird's lifetime. Immature throwers have been seen to throw rocks more than seventy times and then give up in disgust. More mature birds may achieve the skill of one individual which scored 38 direct hits out of 64 tries. It is thought that the Egyptian vulture began its rock-throwing tradition by throwing the eggs of smaller birds on to the ground. Only when it was confronted with the frustration of not being able to carry an enormous ostrich egg aloft did it resort to throwing rocks at it.

The black-breasted buzzard of Australia is reputed to do the same with emu eggs. Aborigines tell of the buzzard chasing the parent emu from the nest and then dropping rocks on the eggs.

The mongoose does it differently. It throws the eggs at a rock. The Egyptian mongoose, a creature considered sacred by the ancient Egyptians, picks up an egg with its forepaws and throws it between its back legs against a large stone being used as an anvil. Thrushes use an anvil to break open snail shells. And ravens and bearded vultures carry large pieces of bone into the air and then drop them on to a hard, rocky surface in order to smash them and get at the marrow. Gulls drop shellfish on to rocks to break them open.

The peregrine falcon ambushes birds in the air. Prey are spotted from a distance and pursued. The peregrine rises above the target and stoops into an attack. The prey may be hit on the back of the head, grabbed in mid-air, forced to the ground or snatched from a cliff edge or treetop. The strong, curved bill serves to tear the meat from the bone. Wood pigeons are the favourite, but prey ranges from goldcrests to herons in size.

◀ The leopard, like all cats, has enlarged canine teeth - longer and stronger than those of dogs - which it can sink into the nape of a victim's neck and dislocate the cervical vertebrae or suffocate it with a killing bite that constricts the trachea.

▼ The menacing teeth of the sand tiger shark fall out quite regularly, but they are replaced by a moving conveyor-belt of new teeth growing up in rows behind.

The cheetah is unlike most other cats for it does not have claws that retract completely. Instead, the claws act like running spikes, giving this champion sprinter a better grip on the ground.

The sharp, curved talons of the red-tailed hawk are typical of a bird of prey. The victim is killed by the claws and the beak is used to tear it apart.

The crown of thorns starfish is eating up the corals of the Great Barrier Reef. It travels slowly but surely across the reef on hundreds of tiny tube feet.

Like an ancient Roman gladiator, the net-throwing spider dangles upside-down and waits for an insect to pass beneath. As a victim passes below, the net is spread and the spider throws it over the prey.

◄

This magnificent spider - one of the bolas spiders of Australia - dangles a sticky glob on a silk thread. Male moths, attracted by a sex odour emitted by the lure, fly close by. The vibrations stimulate the spider to swing the lure like a bolas and the moths are trapped on the sticky secretions. The line is hauled in and the spider has its meal.

▼

Some orb-weaving spiders have enormous webs that not only capture flying insect prey but could also be damaged by passing birds. To warn birds of a 'web ahead', the spider weaves in special zig-zag patterns of silk, known as stabilimenta. This is common in webs that stay up during the day. Spiders without these warnings take their webs down at dawn and remake them at dusk.

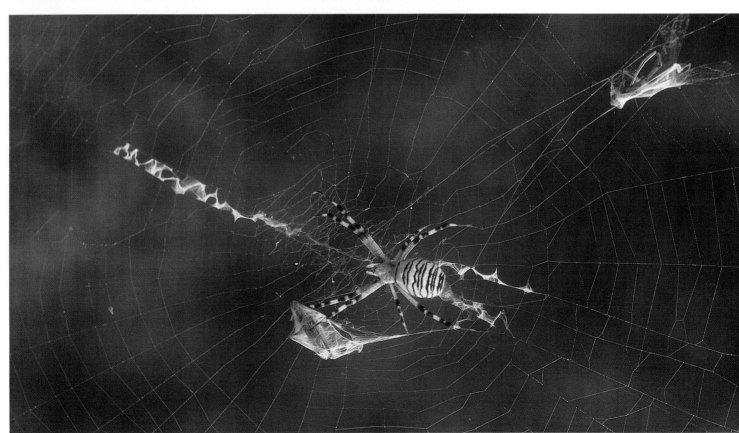

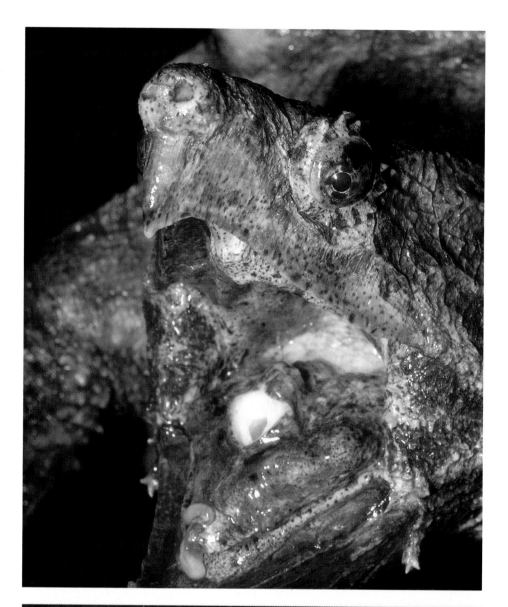

The alligator snapping turtle lies motionless on the lake or river bottom. It sits with its jaws agape, and the only movement is from a worm-like projection on the floor of the mouth (top). Small fish, investigating the prospect of a meal of wriggling aquatic worm, are grabbed. All the turtle need do is close its jaws (bottom).

The archer fish lives in mangrove swamps from India to northern Australia. It knocks insects from branches by spitting at them. The refraction of light is compensated for by the fish positioning itself directly below the target. It is accurate up to 5ft (1.5m). Insects close to the water are grabbed when the fish simply jumps out of the water.

There are no woodpeckers in the Galapagos archipelago, off the coast of Ecuador. But, one of Darwin's famous finches has filled the vacant ecological niche. The woodpecker finch probes for large insects behind bark and in soft, decaying wood. It winkles out those that are difficult to obtain with the help of a twig or a cactus spine.

The black heron has a curious habit of raising its wings over its head like an umbrella or sunshade. Whether the bird is shading its eyes so it is better able to see prey below the surface, or whether it is creating a shaded area under which fish might hide, is not certain.

Green herons have been seen angling for fish. They throw suitable bait-sized pieces of twig, biscuit or anything else that is to hand, and wait for fish to come to the surface to investigate. Some birds have even been seen to fashion their twigs into the right shape and size.

Locating Prey

5

Predators must have finely tuned sensory systems in order to locate their prey. Given that prey animals are built to flee or hide from predators, then predators must be one sensory jump ahead if they are to find a meal. It is the original biological arms race. There are many sensory windows to explore and many stimuli to perceive – sounds, sights, smells, touch, vibrations, movements, electricity and magnetism – and predatory animals have exploited them all.

Prey animals are mobile, some flighty and fast moving, and so a predator must have the ability to find and bring down prey with the minimum of effort. By investing, up front as it were, in a highly evolved sensory system, a predator will reduce the amount of energy it must use in capture and consumption.

Sensory systems must operate initially from a distance, and many predators have the ability to detect and locate prey from afar. Predatory animals are able to detect tiny movements or changes in the disposition of the prey, often changes so slight that they are beyond the sensory capability of humans.

Predators are also aided by having a preconceived image of the prey, the so-called 'search image'. Certain characteristics of the prey automatically trigger off an interest on the part of the predator and might even cause it to start the hunt. These factors might not be constant - spotted hyenas, for instance, might track wildebeest one day and switch to zebra the next - or, they might be very precise. The rufous-naped tamarin likes stick insects, but it only recognises them by the head or legs. If those parts are removed, the insects remain undetected, one reason why stick insects keep their limbs flat against the body.

EAGLE-EYED

BIRDS, LIKE PEOPLE, are essentially visual creatures, and the hunters amongst them use their eyes to find a meal. Birds of prey have big eyes; the ratio of eye size to brain size is much greater than in mammals. Even the smaller hawks have much larger eyes than our own. They can also see a larger picture and in more

This young, female Cooper's hawk at Cape May, New Jersey, has the typical large, forward-facing eyes of a bird of prey.

BIRD'S EYE VIEW

A raptor's retina is endowed with many 'cones', light sensitive cells that not only detect colour but also give greater visual acuity or sharpness. It is thought that a bird of prey has a visual acuity three to four times that of man. The most obvious feature o the face of a bird of prey is the way the eyes face forwards. It has stereoscopic or binocular vision, giving it the ability not only to spot prey but also to know its exact location. An eagle's eyes fit tightly in the eye socket, and so the bird is unable to glance up and down without moving its head. Owls have gone one step further. Their eyes fill all the available head space and are tubular in shape. And instead of moving its eyes, an owl can turn its head, rather comically, almost through 360 degrees. It also gives rise to the curious bobbing behaviour when an owl spots something in the distance and moves its head up and down and side to side in order to assess its position. Eagles will even turn the head upside down.

detail. The transparent cornea at the front of the eye is flat, unlike the curved cornea that we have. This allows more of the field of vision to be in focus, unlike the limited centre-spot focus that we can see. At the back of the eye, on the light-sensitive retina, birds have a greater number of light receptor cells than we do. They are known as the 'rods', and we have about 200,000 per square millimetre of retina. Even the tiny sparrow does better than that - it has 400,000. But the hawks have an amazing 1,000,000 on every square millimetre, giving them a high-definition view of the world about which we can only dream.

Another secret weapon in a hawk, falcon or eagle's eye is the fovea, of which raptors have two. These are the points of sharpest vision, where the density of cones is greatest. They give a bird a visual image that is, perhaps, eight times as acute as our own. They help a hunting bird to perceive distance, an essential function for a bird, like a peregrine, hurtling at prey at 100mph or more.

With eyes like these, a bird of prey is a formidable predator, capable of amazing feats. In tests, the kestrel has been found to be able to spot a mouse from a height of a mile (1.6km) above the ground. And a martial eagle - one of the largest of Africa's eagles - was once seen to take off from a hill 4 miles (6.4km) from an unsuspecting guineafowl, only to swoop down and carry it away. The best a person could do, without binoculars, is to see the same sized bird at a mile and no further.

Birds that dive into water after prey, like the kingfisher, also have two foveas, and they enable the bird to adjust its eyes above and below water. Light behaves differently in air and water. This is why a stick, standing in water, looks bent. For a bird, diving at high speed to catch a small, thin, well-disguised fish, this could be a serious drawback. To overcome the problem, a second 'aquatic' fovea compensates for the change in conditions as the bird enters the water, ensuring that it is successful in capturing its prey.

The mammalian equivalent of the bird's sophisticated visual system is known as the 'visual streak'. Lions and other cats do not have a central fovea, as we do, but a broadly horizontal band of ultrasensitive light receptors. This increases visual acuity horizontally so that cats are better able to see the position and movement of prey on the ground. They do not need to be that much aware of things above and below, only events happening ahead. The cheetah takes this to an extreme with a very narrow strip of nerve cells across the retina, enabling it to see its prey clearly against the horizon.

Other smaller animals with well-developed eyes include the praying mantis, the similarly-named mantid shrimp, and the chameleon. Each has the ability to move its eyes independently of each other and in all directions. But when prey is located, both eyes are brought to bear on the target, giving binocular vision with greater accuracy in securing a meal.

For some animals, sight is essential for prey capture, but a precise and detailed picture seems unnecessary. An angel shark lies dormant on the bottom of the sea until the movement of a fish nearby triggers it to rise up like some gigantic monster with an enormous open mouth and swallow the passer-by whole. Frogs, toads and day-hunting snakes also respond only to movement. As long as a slug remains still, a toad will ignore it. If it is in gulping distance, however, and it moves, the toad will grab it. The European whip snake relies on the movements of its prey in order to catch it. The snake will follow a frog intently through the reeds as long as it is moving. If it stops, the snake stops; if it moves, the snake pursues until it can reach out and grab the fleeing prey.

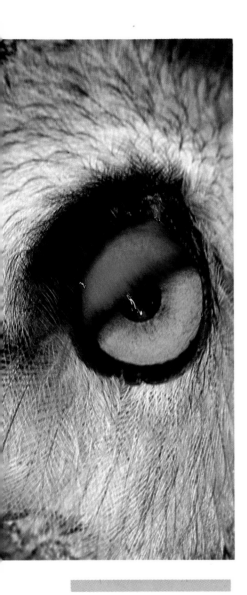

The eye of a long-eared owl is so large and its tubular shape takes up so much room in the eye socket that it is unable to turn. The owl can only move its eye if it moves its head.

Some species of snakes rely on wavelengths of light that we 'feel' rather than see. Pit-vipers and rattlesnakes, for example, have pits in the nose containing membranes sensitive to infra-red radiation or heat. They can appreciate changes in temperature as minute as 0.005 degrees C. In pitch darkness, a rattlesnake can detect the presence of a mouse, just as long as the unfortunate rodent approaches to within 6in (15cm) of the snake's snout. Boas and pythons have the same kind of heat receptors on the lips.

Kingfishers have eyes adapted for seeing above and below the water surface. Watching for fish from a perch or by hovering over the water, a bird plunges into the water at an angle of about 45 degrees. At the moment of impact a nictitating membrane covers and protects the eye.

SMELL

REPTILES, SUCH AS SNAKES and lizards, more usually 'taste' the air for evidence of food nearby. Chemicals on the wind are trapped on the moist tongue and pressed against the Jacobson's organ, a pair of cavities, lined with sensory cells, in the roof of the mouth near the snout. Monitor, beaded and whiptailed lizards, with long, forked-tongues, have a better developed sense of smell than their broad-tongued relatives. The gigantic, 10ft (3m) long, Komodo dragons of the islands of Indonesia depend on an acute sense of smell to track down their prey, often wild deer, pigs and feral goats. They lie in wait, hidden in bushes or scrub, flicking their tongue in and out until the tell-tale smell of prey is near. Although large and bulky, weighing up to 365lb (165kg), these enormous beasts are surprisingly agile and can hijack an unwary animal. They have even been known to follow a pregnant goat, waiting patiently until she drops her kid before they race in, grab the new-born and rip it apart as they wrestle for a morsel.

More often, Komodo dragons will home-in on carrion, the irresistible smells of a putrifying carcass acting as an olfactory beacon for every dragon within smelling distance. But those other consumers of dead bodies, the Old World vultures, do not use smell to find a corpse, as was once suspected; rather, they use sight. And if one spots food, the very act of dropping down to eat it attracts all the other vultures in the neighbourhood and a large, noisy, squabbling flock soon forms.

The enormous Komodo dragon, the largest lizard in the world, relies on smell to find its food. It 'tastes' the air with its tongue,

Some of the New World vultures, on the other hand, do use smell, and in doing so have been able to search for food in inaccessible places, such as forests, where a carcass would normally be hidden. The turkey vulture, related more to the stork than to birds of prey, is thought to have a well-developed sense of smell, an ability that makes it a buddy of the king vulture. The king vulture seems not to possess the skill and relies on the commotion caused by turkey vultures and other scavengers to locate a carcass.

The expert smell-seeker of the bird world is the New Zealand kiwi. It is nocturnal, flightless, has a long, probing snout and hair-like feathers, and to all intents and purposes looks like a mammal. Indeed, the kiwi is often described as an 'honorary' mammal, playing the role of the European hedgehog. It feeds by snuffling about in the forest litter, smelling out earthworms and other invertebrates of the forest floor.

TOUCH

DABBLING DUCKS and probing plovers use touch to find prey. The number of touch receptors or corpuscles in the end of the bill of these birds exceeds even the nerve endings in the human finger-tip. Using this sense, most waders can blindly explore sand and mud, and avocets are able to sweep ahead of them, snapping up any tiny aquatic creature it might touch. Spoonbills work with curious-shaped bills in the same way.

Woodpeckers have touch-sensitive cells at the tip of the tongue. With these, they can explore the tunnels of wood-boring insects and insect larvae. Once located, the juicy morsel is hooked out by the bird's barbed and sticky tongue.

The most extraordinary reliance on touch is, perhaps, shown by the skimmer. This remarkable, tern-like bird seems to have its bill built upside down: the long mandible is at the bottom and the shorter one at the top. Seen head-on, it is very thin and is built to offer minimum resistance. The bird feeds by flying up and down with its head very close to the water. The bottom mandible cuts through the surface, hence the name 'skimmer', until it makes contact with a fish. Automatically, the bill snaps shut and the head drops down, trapping the fish sideways between the scissors of the bill; it is then lifted from the water. If an object, like a rock, offers slightly more resistance, then the head bends round and special muscles in the neck lessen the shock. Using this method of fishing, the skimmer is only able to feed on lagoons, lakes and at the sides of wide, slow-moving rivers. It is restricted to times when the water is mirror-calm, often at dawn, dusk and through the night. It takes advantage of the fact that it is about when there is no competition from other birds.

Also on the calm water-surface might be water-striders (pond skaters), back swimmers, whirligig beetles and clawed toads. All these creatures are in close contact with the surface film and are able to locate prey, trapped in the surface tension, by the tell-tale ripples that emanate from their struggling bodies.

Under the sea, starfish and sea-urchins creep about on the sea-floor and use touch, together with a sense of smell, to find and to examine a prospective meal. At the bottom of the deep sea, bright red prawns with exceptionally long feelers and deep-sea fishes with long, under-chin barbels, many times the length of the body, are thought to use these structures, not only to find their way about like a blind man with a stick, but also to make contact with food.

In the darkness of caves, sight is inappropriate to the extent that many cave creatures have lost their eyes altogether, and can range from blind crickets and cave-fish to blind salamanders. Some rely on smell, but many have adaptations of parts of the body to afford a better sense of touch. Voracious cave crickets and earwigs have long antennae, as have poisonous, spindly-legged centipedes and giant, 6in-across, red-eyed spiders.

Their surface-living, web-weaving counterparts are also touch experts. Hiding behind a leaf at the side of its circular web, a garden spider rests one leg on a tension line and waits for a flying insect to blunder in. If the vibrations are too great, the spider will ignore the signal and hope that the giant it has caught will work itself free and fall out. If they are just right, it will dash out and immobilise its prey with a single, poisonous bite.

SHOCKING TAIL

SOME ANIMAL HUNTERS have utilised and enhanced the electrical function of nerves and muscles for prey detection and, in some extreme cases, even prey debilitation.

A group of freshwater fishes, known as the weak-electric fishes, surround themselves with an electric field which can be turned on and off at will. In turbid waters, the fish can use the field to find their way about, but they can also communicate with it and investigate potential items of food. The field is generated by modified muscles or nerves depending on the species. The 8in (20cm) long, elephant trunk fish and the South African and South American

Woodpeckers, like this hairy woodpecker of North and Central America, have a long, barbed tongue with which they can detect (by touch) and extract wood-boring grubs and other insects from holes in a tree-trunk.

knife fishes have modified axial and tail muscles.

Electro-location works very simply by an object in the water interfering with the lines of the electrical field. Depending on its electrical properties, the object is detected by the battery of sensory cells all over the fish's body. Some fish enhance their electrical image by developing focusing systems. Knife fishes tend to bend their bodies around the object being investigated, whereas elephant fishes swim backwards and forwards, scanning the object and increasing the pulse rate of their electrical discharges to gain more detailed information. The small, weak-electric fishes locate and eat tiny, aquatic insect larvae and worms, but the larger species will attack small fish.

At the other end of the scale are the 'strong' electric fishes - the stunning electric eel of the Amazon, the electric catfish of Africa, and the formidable

The electric eel of South American rivers grows to 5ft (1¹/₂m) long and is found in holes in the river-bank. It finds its way about and locates prey in the turbid waters with electricity.

electric torpedo ray of the shallow sea. These fish not only locate their prey with electricity, but also store such an enormous charge that they can knock out an adult person in one almighty discharge.

The electric ray was known by the ancient Greeks, and its Greek name 'narke' or numbfish gave rise to our currently used word 'narcotic'. The numbfish was thought of as a magical beast, bewitching its prey and any unfortunate fisherman who happened to tangle with it. The ancients believed that a pregnant woman was assured an easy birth if a numbfish was placed in the delivery room.

Today, the electric ray is as revered as it was in the time of Socrates. Growing to over 6ft (2m) and weighing over 200lb (90kg), the torpedo ray produces and stores its electrical charge in two, large blocks of modified muscle on either side of the flattened body. Discharges of up to 220 volts have been recorded. The fish can make an electric light bulb glow, but only on the first few attacks. The electric organ is quickly spent and the fish must retire, quite literally, to recharge its batteries.

The freshwater electric catfish, which can grow to 3.3ft (1m) in length and weigh up to 44lb (20kg), delivers a 350-450 volt blow, and the 9ft (2.75m) long electric eel - not an eel at all, but a relative of the minnow - is capable of delivering a staggering 550 volts, not just once or twice, but several times a minute for as long as it wants.

SOUND SYSTEMS

THE BIG EARS are a giveaway. Fennec and bat-eared foxes and aardwolfs use their ears to detect infinitesimally small sounds such as the comings and goings of termites underground. Mainly at night, bat-eared foxes, from southern Africa, dash about their feeding area, stopping occasionally to put an ear to the ground in order to pick up the scrabbling sounds of insect activity. They have a particular fondness for harvester termites, but failing that a scorpion or beetle

Termites do not make a lot of noise, but the bat-eared fox, with its enormous ears, can hear them scrabbling about below the surface. Having detected the termites, the fox digs down to them.

larva will do. Once found, the termite procession causes a flurry of digging as the fox excavates its evening meal. In the dry season, when prey is scarce, the ears are also alert for marauding lions and brown hyenas, and they help ensure that this small predator does not become the prey.

Sound, not unexpectedly, is important to night hunters. Nocturnal owls, like fennec foxes, hunt by detecting incredibly quiet sounds, such as the rustling of a mouse or vole through the undergrowth. But they don't have big ears - even the 'ears' of the long-eared owl are not functional and are only used for display; instead, the owl's entire face is designed to receive sound. The heart-shaped facial disc of tightly packed feathers in the barn owl resembles a pair of parabolic reflectors, of the kind used by wildlife sound recordists to pick up sounds that are far away. Sounds hitting the owl's face are focused on each ear and, in the same way that the forward-pointing eyes give the bird stereoscopic vision to locate visual movement, the arrangement of the facial disc gives the bird the ability to receive stereophonic sound and pinpoint the source of those sounds. The ears are also set one slightly above the other, on either side of the face, which gives the owl up-and-down as well as horizontal information. The

The long-eared bat, as its name suggests, has big ears. It is one of the 'gleaner' bats that sometimes locates insect prey by listening for movements of the body, such as wingbeats.

result is an amazingly accurate system of prey location that works in total darkness.

Bats have overcome hunting at night in a different way. They do not listen for the sounds made by the prey; rather, they produce their own, very high-frequency sounds and listen for the echoes that bounce back, a behaviour known as echolocation.

A small, insect-eating bat, such as a noctule, cruising about in no kind of hurry, ensures that it does not bump into anything by producing pulses of echolocation sound 5-20 times a second. If an echo from something to eat is received, the pulse-rate goes up to, say, 50 times a second. As the bat homes-in on its target, jigging rapidly this way and that, it needs even more detailed information about size, speed and direction of the prey and increases its sound emissions to a buzz containing 200 or more pulses per second. It is critical for the bat to have this data for its manoeuvres in the dark must be more precise. To help gain even more information, the bat can adjust its call frequency. Many of the small bats, known as 'FM' bats (which stands for frequency modulation), sweep their echolocation sounds downwards at the end of each pulse. In doing so they extend the band width of their signal and gain extra information about the whereabouts of the target.

The greater horseshoe bat does it differently. It is one of the 'doppler' bats, and any motorist caught speeding by doppler radar will understand how effectively it works. This prey location system operates, not by looking at the time taken for the echolocation signal to bounce back, but by comparing the frequency of the returning signal with that of the outgoing. A bat knows what frequency it sent out, but the frequency coming back will be a little different if the prey is moving with respect to the bat - a phenomenon known as the Doppler Effect. In short, if the target is moving away, the frequency of the returning signal drops, but if the prey is coming towards the bat, the frequency goes up. The difference in frequency between the transmitted signal and the echo is, therefore, a means of measuring the relative motion of the predator and prey; an amazing calculation for a little bat to be able to do.

Doppler bats, like the greater horseshoe, have a less frantic hunting tactic than the noctule. It remains stationary, sometimes at the roost site, rotating its head and scanning the surrounding area with a narrow beam of sound, much like a ground-to-air-missile radar. When a contact is made, the bat flies out, catches it and returns to the launch site.

Some bats, like the European pipistrelle, make use of both methods depending on the circumstances. It is the commonest of British bats and is the one usually seen flying just above the head on a summer's evening. At the start of a hunt, the bat needs to survey as large an area as possible and can do so with a long, low-frequency signal from which it can receive back a useful 'Doppler' signal. This gives it good information about the speed of a target and the direction it is heading but little about its actual distance from the bat. So, having made contact, the bat switches to the 'FM' system, emitting increasingly faster pulses of frequency sweeps until the target insect is caught.

Most of the small bats hunt by echolocation using very high-frequency signals (ultrasounds), but there are some that break the rules. These are the 'gleaners'. The pallid bat of North America is a gleaner. Instead of emitting its own sounds, it listens for the sounds made by the prey. Moths and other flying insects 'warm-up' before take-off. They must raise the temperature of their flight muscles before they can fly efficiently and the pallid bat homes-in on the wing vibrations.

Another rule breaker lives in the Central American rainforest, but it ignores the rich variety of jungle insects in favour of tiny frogs. The fringe-lipped bat is fond of mud-puddle frogs, and it has discovered that the location of its favourite prey can be found by listening to the mating calls. The bat navigates through the forest using normal high-frequency echolocation, but on picking up the calls of the frog, it switches off, homing-in on the lower-frequency calls of the frog. The fringe-lip sweeps down, grabs the frog in its mouth and heads for home.

KILLING WITH SOUND

DOLPHINS AND THEIR toothed whale relatives locate prey by echolocation. Indeed, a dolphin can 'see' with sound, and there is evidence that it can also kill with sound.

By bouncing high-frequency sounds off an underwater target and analysing the signal it gets back, a dolphin can accurately locate an object, determine whether and where it is moving, discriminate different object densities, say, fat from bone, can tell whether a target is dead or alive, and if alive and potential food may be able to stun it, and sometimes kill it with a high-intensity beam of sound.

The sounds, mostly clicks and bursts of clicks, are produced by pushing air backwards and forwards through a complicated plumbing system at the back of the nostrils. The sounds pass through the fatty, bulbous 'melon' in the forehead, where they are focused into a narrow beam of ultrasound. The returning echo is picked up by the teeth of the lower jaw and the signal transmitted through the jaw and up to the brain. Using the system a trained dolphin can distinguish a tangerine from a small metal ball at a distance of 370ft (113m). In laboratory

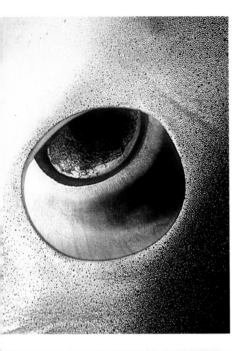

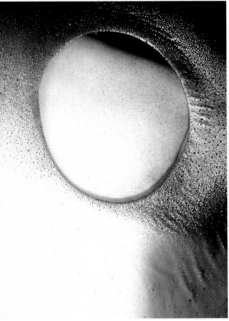

A protective nictitating membrane covers the eye of a blue shark as it is about to attack.

tests, dolphins have produced such powerful sounds that they are close to the finite limit of sound. Any louder and they would turn to heat. With such a weapon, dolphins are formidable killers.

They use their sound system first to locate schools of fish or squid, and then they spray them with high-intensity sounds. Striped dolphins have been seen to circle an anchovy school, zap them with sound, and then cut through the debilitated fish, shovelling them into their jaws at will. Near Vancouver, a similar observation was made with killer whales. A large salmon was clearly visible swimming in the water next to a fishing boat. Along came a pod of killer whales and the salmon was stopped dead in its tracks. One of the whales scooped up the salmon and swam on. Had it been stopped by sound? Perhaps it was, but evidence from another relative of the dolphins seems to suggest that killing with sound is reality rather than speculation.

The biggest of the toothed whales is the sperm whale, with an omnibus-sized body and an enormous fatty body in its forehead, known as the spermaceti organ. Sperm whales, like dolphins, produce echolocation clicks, and they go hunting in the deep sea. Their favourite prey seems to be giant squid, the world's largest invertebrates that may grow to 70ft long (measured from tentacle tip to body tip) and which have rarely been seen alive. Most specimens have either been washed up dead on the shore or found as pieces in the stomachs of sperm whales caught by whaling ships.

The curious thing, though, is that some whales have been caught that show malformations of the lower jaw, yet their stomachs are filled with squid. The theory is that the squid are zapped with enormous quantities of ultrasound and, thus neutralised, their inert bodies are slurped in by the whale. Tests have shown that squid can be killed with high-intensity blasts of sound, and researchers listening with underwater microphones to hunting sperm whales have reported them producing very loud, rifle-like cracks that are thought to be salvos of killing sound. The large, saucer-sized, sucker marks on the heads of some sperm whales are witness to the giants who did not succumb to the sound bombardment and tried to fight back.

THE ULTIMATE PREDATOR

SHARKS, CONTRARY TO popular belief, are not primitive. The 250 known species living today are the product of 350 million years of evolution, time enough for some of the most sophisticated hunting systems to be developed and honed to perfection. The mackerel sharks - the great white, mako and porbeagle - the hammerheads, and the aptly named requiem sharks, including the notorious bull shark, the oceanic whitetip, whalers and reef sharks, are, perhaps, the ultimate killing machines. They are programmed to seek out and eat, and are aided in this dedicated task by the most diverse array of sensory mechanisms used by any predator.

A shark might first be alerted to the sounds of a struggling fish. Low-frequency sounds (40Hz and below) can travel vast distances through the water and sharks can be attracted to a target from over a mile away. At a quarter of a mile, a shark can smell blood or body fluids in the water, and follow an olfactory corridor to head upcurrent. Taking a zig-zag course the shark samples the water for the areas of greatest concentration and gradually follows the odour trail towards the victim. It can detect one part of tuna extract in 25 million parts of water; that's the equivalent of 10 drops in an average-sized swimming-pool.

At about 100yds (100m), the shark's lateral-line system might play a role. It consists of a row of fluid-filled sensory canals running along either side of the head and body. Tiny hairs in the canals are sensitive to vibrations, pressure changes and movements, so the shark can almost 'feel' the presence and location of something moving in the water. It is also able to compare minute differences in the current flow on either side of the body. Together with the information it is receiving from its olfactory system, the shark can more accurately locate a target upstream.

At about 75ft (23m), and almost in the dark, the shark can begin to see the movement of its prey, and in colour. Its eyes are ten times more sensitive to dim light than ours, and it can discriminate between blue, blue-green and yellow. If heading rapidly to the surface, like a great white attacking an elephant seal, the shark can switch off its dark-adapted system and function normally in bright light.

The grey reef shark is one of the 'requiem' sharks. It grows to about 8ft (2.5m) and can be aggressive to humans. Like all sharks, it uses multiple senses to locate and catch prey.

As it closes for the final attack the eyes are protected. In some sharks, a membrane slides across; in others, such as the great white, the eyes recede into the safety of the socket. Essentially, the shark is now swimming blind, but it has one more remarkable sensory system to bring into play, one that detects electricity. Sensory organs, located in small, jelly-filled pits in the snout, can detect minute electric currents associated with muscle activity, such as the beating heart or gill movements, in the prey. The sensitivity to the electric field surrounding a prey fish is so great that a shark can detect a change in intensity of a hundred-millionth of a volt per centimetre, the equivalent of a flashlight battery creating a field between two electrodes 1,000 miles apart.

The hammerhead sharks, with their curious T-shaped head, make full use of this system. By spreading the electroreceptors along the width of the head, they are able to scan a wider area and more accurately detect prey, such as flatfish, skates and rays buried in the sand.

And if that's not enough, sharks are thought to be able to detect the lines of force in the earth's magnetic field, so that a wandering great white can be in the right place, at the right time, in order to be ready to grab a meal.

A greater mouse-eared bat, with a wingspan of up to 18in (45cm), is one of Europe's largest bats. It often takes non-flying, ground-living insects, like crickets and ground beetles.

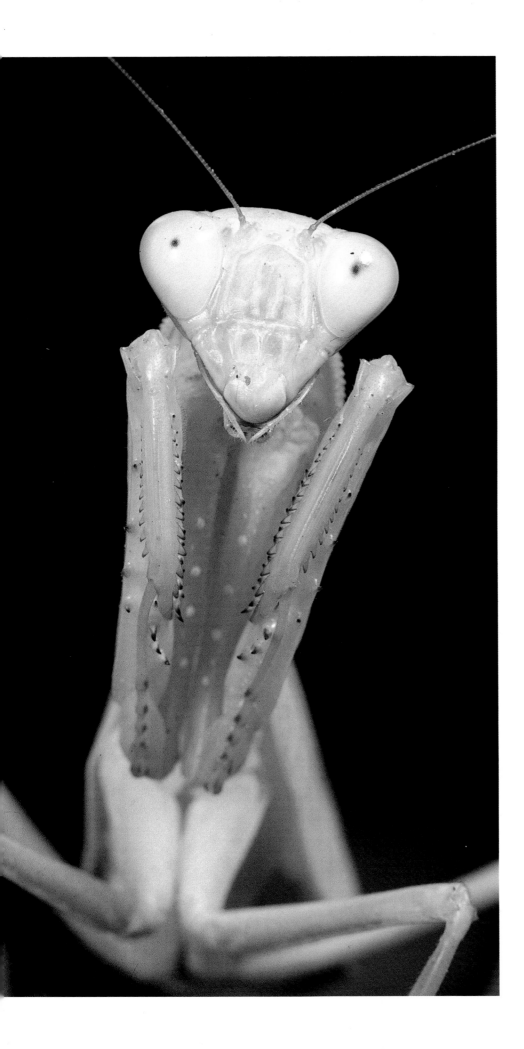

The barn owl has a facial disc which can focus sounds at the ears. In this way it can hear the slightest rustling in the grass and catch itself a vole.

Rattlesnakes, like this giant tropical species known as the cascabel from Central and South America, have pits in the snout with which they can detect the heat given off by warm-bodied prey, such as mice.

The praying mantis has large eyes, affording this voracious predator keen eyesight. It lies in wait for prey, its arms folded (as if in prayer). If an insect should stray too close, the mantis slowly turns its head and top of its body to face the target. Suddenly, the spiny arms shoot out and grab it.

▶

The elephant trunk fish of West Africa finds its way about in turbid waters by surrounding itself with a low-voltage electric field. Obstacles, such as other trunk fish or prey that disturb the field, can be detected.

▶

The flightless kiwi is an honorary mammal. A native of New Zealand, it fills the same ecological niche reserved for the hedgehog in Europe. It probes the ground with its long bill and finds its food with a highly developed sense of smell.

▼

A common starfish from Florida waters uses the senses of smell and touch to detect the presence of a flame scallop. If it is lucky and can trap the scallop, it is able to pull two shells apart using its sucker feet. The scallop, however, is able to escape by clapping its shells together and moving by jet-propulsion.

Speed

6

After the target has been located and tracked, and the sensory systems have played their role, the period of watching and waiting is over. It is time to act; all or nothing, the moment when a predator must decide whether to go or not. And when it does so, it must move fast. At the moment of capture, a pursuer must be faster than the pursued, and to achieve this superiority the predator might use its entire body or just a part of it. For those predators that ambush, lie in wait or set traps, speed of movement is seen in, say, specialised limbs, a telescopic tongue or extensible jaws. Speed of movement is difficult to assess or record, but with modern instrumentation many of the myths are being disproved and the fastest predators are found to be running, flying or swimming at speeds much less than was originally thought. Nevertheless, there are some speedy hunters. The fastest land mammal is undoubtedly the cheetah, the fastest bird is considered to be the peregrine falcon, the fastest whale or dolphin is the killer whale, the fastesty land reptile recorded so far is the six-lined race runner of North America, and the contenders for the fastest swimming fish are the sailfish and the bluefin tuna. The fastest movement in the natural world is thought to be the discharge of the sting of a sea-anemone or jellyfish.

FASTEST RUNNERS

THE CHEETAH IS small-headed, long-legged and built for speed. It carries no surplus weight, has an amazingly flexible backbone and the smallest head, in relation to its body, of any cat. It is, without doubt, the world's fastest land animal, attaining 45mph (72km/h) in 3 seconds, from a standing start, and reaching a top speed of up to 60mph (97km/h). But it has no stamina. The chase must be short. Indeed, only half of a cheetah's chases are successful, an average pursuit being over 550ft (170m) and lasting just 20 seconds. If the pursuer has not caught up with the pursued by then, it aborts the attack.

It differs from many of the other cats in that it hunts by day, and although it prefers the cooler hours at dawn and at dusk, it has heat problems. With such a powerful set of running muscles, the cheetah generates enormous amounts of heat. In a 200yd dash, its body temperature can rise to 105 degrees F (41 degrees C), a level certain to cause brain damage if sustained for more than a minute or two. The animal's answer is twofold: either, it ambles nonchalantly towards the prey, freezing each time the animal looks up, or it uses stealth to approach its victim, most likely a Thompson's gazelle, before a sudden, rapid burst of speed to make the capture. The critical distance is about 50yds. If the cheetah can make it to that point without 'spooking' the gazelle, it is in with a chance and will take off on the short, high-speed chase.

The fleeing prey jinks from side to side, but the cheetah continues in a straight, accelerating line. It must anticipate the prey's route of escape and intercept it. There is an alternative strategy. If the prey is slower than the cheetah, it starts by sprinting after it but then simply follows the zig-zags, moving at less than maximum speed but for longer. The final attack is preceded by one last burst, when the victim is running away. As the cheetah catches up,

The cheetah is the fastest land animal over a short distance, but it cannot keep going for long. If the prey can keep ahead for long enough, the cheetah will soon give up and must rest.

HIGH-SPEED HUNTERS

The fastest land predators are the sprinters. They have light, lean and supple bodies set on long, powerful legs perfect for short bursts of speed but not built for stamina. Land predators as diverse as hunting spiders and big cats get tired quickly, so the final dash is often the culmination of a carefully orchestrated build-up of stealthy tracking and surveillance. But at the moment of take-off, enormous amounts of pent-up energy are released to make these animals some of the fastest creatures on 2, 4, 6 or 8 legs. In the air, fast flying is achieved with specialised wings and powerful flight muscles. In the sea, a torpedo-shaped body is propelled through the relatively dense medium of water by water-adapted limbs or hydrodynamically efficient tails. Interestingly, many fast-moving aerial and aquatic predators have reached the same evolutionary conclusion for wing or fin development. The crescent-shaped wings of the swift and swallow are mirrored in the fins of the shark and the flukes of a dolphin.

it swipes the gazelle's back legs from under it, straddles the struggling body, and suffocates the unfortunate creature with a strong bite to the neck.

Surprisingly, the cheetah does not eat immediately, but waits for about 15 minutes before tucking in. It is so drained of energy and overheated that it must sit and pant in order to cool down. When at last it is ready, the food is bolted down; after all, there are other predators ready to steal a kill. The cheetah, being a slender, lightly built cat, has no defence against a leopard, hyena or lion. Even vultures have been known to drive a cheetah from its meal.

In the bird world, the roadrunner, as its name implies, is also a sprinter. It lives in the arid, desert chaparral of the south-western part of North America. It **can** fly, but prefers to pursue its lizard, snake and invertebrate prey on the ground. Paced by a car, the roadrunner has been attributed with speeds of over 26mph (42km/h). It runs, almost arrogantly, with a straight neck, its wings slightly open as stabilisers, its legs going at 12 steps a second and its tail used as a rudder that can turn the bird through 90 degrees without slowing down.

Fast-moving insects are fair game to the roadrunner, but some insects use their speed, not to run away, but to pursue their own food. The tiger beetle is

The roadrunner of the Mojave Desert has been immortalised in an animated cartoon of the same name and its fictional speed is more than matched by its real performance across the desert floor in pursuit of lizards and insects.

Britain's swiftest animal on 6 legs. It is capable of sprinting over short distances and has been timed at 24in/s (60cm/s), about one and a bit miles per hour. This may seem slow, but this small ½in (15mm) long beetle is actually going at 40 body lengths per second, the equivalent of a racehorse travelling at 200mph. It is a voracious predator. Equipped with large eyes and sharply pointed jaws, it intercepts insects on open, sandy heathland, and, although it can fly, prefers to chase its prey on the ground.

The fastest known land invertebrates have not 6, but 8 long legs, although they only use 6 for running; they are the sun or wind spiders, not spiders at all, but close relations of scorpions. Sun spiders are particularly aggressive predators, using fang-like pincers to crush prey, the vibrations of which are picked up by sensory organs on the fourth pair of legs. In pursuit, the sun spider can clock up an estimated 10mph (16km/h). It places its first pair of legs out in front where they act as 'feelers'.

STOOPING OUT OF THE SKY

THE PEREGRINE FALCON sets up an ambush in the sky. Waiting in the clouds about a mile above the ground it spots a target below. It folds back its wings and drops. During the 'stoop', it can reach speeds of over 100mph - any faster and it would be out of control - making it the fastest living thing on earth. It approaches its target from above and behind, taking advantage of a blind spot directly behind the prey's head. On contact it either grabs with its powerful, yellow talons or strikes down at the victim with a single blow that, in a flurry of feathers, breaks the prey's neck. Small birds are sometimes snatched in mid-air, plucked and consumed, while the peregrine is still flying.

Swifts and swallows are mean flyers too. They whiz about the sky, aided by their aerodynamically perfect, crescent-shaped wings, catching flying insects. Swifts, like miniature basking sharks, fly with mouth agape, gathering in the aerial 'plankton'.

The speed with which insects themselves fly is difficult to check, but blood-sucking horseflies in pursuit of cars, mistaking them, perhaps, for large, warm-blooded mammals, have reached 31mph (50km/h). Another fly - the botfly, whose larvae eat through the hides of living horses and deer - was credited with reaching 800mph (1,287km/h), a speed quoted by many of the old record books but one which would require the insect to eat astronomical quantities of food - one and a half times its body weight per second - to provide the energy that such a flight would demand. More likely the botfly clocks in at a more modest speed of 30mph (48km/h), itself no mean feat for a tiny insect.

Flying insects that catch other flying insects need a good speed to catch their

The peregrine is reputed to be the fastest animal in the world. Dropping through the air with wings folded but held slightly away from the body, this speedy aerial predator stoops on its target at speeds estimated to be over 100mph. But only one in ten stoops are successful.

prey. The fastest appear to be the dragonflies, the hawks of the insect world, which have been clocked at speeds around 36mph (58km/h). Indeed, one group is called the 'hawker' dragonflies, and like their relatives the 'darters', they have large, effective eyes that can spot prey from 33ft (10m) away.

The hawkers attack on the wing, while the darters launch out from a resting place. Both catch flying insects that inadvertently fly into their territory, and they do it with the legs. The thorax, to which the legs are attached, is angled forwards so that the legs can form a spiny basket in which the prey is caught in mid-air. The victim is taken back to a favourite perch and eaten. The crunching sounds are audible to our ears from several yards away. With large prey items, such as butterflies (and sometimes other smaller dragonflies), only the body is eaten, and the wings discarded. Small items, such as midges and mosquitoes, may be caught and eaten without the dragonfly touching down.

Robber flies also patrol a regular beat, their acute vision and rapid, manoeuvrable flight enabling them to outfly other flying insects. The mouth-parts are modified as sharp, armour-piercing hollow swords with which they can extract body fluids and suck a fly dry.

WARM MUSCLES, WARM BRAINS

SOME SHARKS HAVE warm muscles. The powerful swimming muscles of the great white shark, and its relatives the mako and porbeagle, are kept 45-50 degrees F (7-10 degrees C) warmer than the surrounding seawater. And for each 10 degrees rise in temperature, the shark obtains a threefold increase in muscle power, a useful evolutionary trick to have up your sleeve in keeping one step ahead of your prey.

The shark achieves this with a special blood-supply system to the swimming muscles. In dissection, it looks rather like an old-fashioned, central-heating radiator, and it acts as a heat exchanger. Basically, warm blood is prevented from being carried to places, such as the gills, where heat would be lost to the outside.

A shark's swimming efficiency is further enhanced by the familiar torpedo-shape of its body, and also by the texture of its skin. The skin is covered with minute teeth, known as dermal denticles, which not only give protection, but also lessen a shark's resistance in the water by reducing drag. Designers are experimenting with tiny ribulets on aircraft wings to give them better aerodynamic properties. It has already been found that the addition of ribulets helps increase fuel efficiency. For us, this is a very recent discovery; sharks made the connection many millions of years ago.

The fastest of the sharks is the 12ft (3.7m) long, warm-muscled mako, which, when hooked, has been seen to leap clear of the sea, leaving the water at an estimated 46mph (74km/h).

Tuna have warm muscles too, and when travelling at speed, they pull their fins into grooves along the body, giving them a smooth, hydrodynamic outline. Bluefin tuna are the fastest. They can swim at over 40mph (64km/h) over short distances, most likely escaping from one of their main enemies, the swordfish.

The swordfish is another active undersea predator. It swims in short, fast bursts in pursuit of fast-swimming prey. It does not have warm muscles, though; instead, it has a heater in its head. The brain, the retina of the eye and brown tissue on the underside of the brain case can be up to 57 degrees F (14 degrees C) warmer than the surrounding seawater. Like the great white shark, the swordfish has a heat-exchange mechanism that prevents any serious loss of heat from the blood and directs that warm blood, not towards the muscles, but towards the brain.

Little is known about the biology of the swordfish. It lives mostly in semi-darkness, swimming down to 1,968ft (600m) by day and returning to the surface at night. It does not swim continuously, but, like the cheetah, is known as a 'stalker and sprinter'. If it is to remain alert and ready to respond to opportunities that might present themselves, it must have a sensory system that can respond immediately. And this is precisely what the swordfish has. In order to spot and chase after passing food, particularly in the cold depths, the fish warms up its eyes and brain, an ability it shares with the white marlin and the sailfish, acknowledged by sea anglers to be the fastest fish in the sea.

Swordfish and their relatives go so fast that sometimes they cannot stop. Confronted with a sudden obstacle, a swordfish can be in trouble. The broken swords of swordfish have been found embedded in whales and wooden ships. Predators in the open sea, though, can normally afford to overshoot the mark, but those attacking prey close to the bottom are in danger of crashing into the mud. The large-mouthed bass swims slowly towards its target, using vision to guide it in. At the last moment, it darts at the prey, oblivious to any change of course. If the prey moves, the bass misses, but it is careful not to overshoot the original spot. It makes rapid breaking movements just before the actual point of prey capture so as not to crash.

UNDERWATER PURSUIT

SPEED UNDERWATER IS not confined to the fishes. Some of those animals, like penguins, dolphins and whales, that returned to the sea many millions of years ago, have evolved the necessity for rapid swimming in order to catch their food. The fastest of the sea mammals is the orca or killer whale. Whilst chasing minke whales, themselves capable of escape speeds of over 30mph (48km/h), orcas have been seen to swim at 40mph (64km/h). Their smaller relatives, the dolphins, can also turn on the speed. Common dolphins have been timed at 27mph (44km/h) and many other species do just as well. And all this with an up-and-down movement of the tail flukes rather than the side-to-side movement characteristic of fish.

Penguins 'fly' underwater. Their wings turn into flippers and they can dart about at around 10mph (16km/h). In order to gain even more speed, penguins and dolphins adopt a similar 'porpoising' behaviour, periodically leaping clear of the water. At a certain speed, depending on the size and shape of the swimmer, the pressure wave formed in front of the head offers so much resistance that it would be counterproductive to try to swim hard. Instead, the animal uses the energy to push clear of the water. Once in the air, it faces less resistance. By porpoising, penguins and dolphins have the best of both worlds and can travel faster and further for the same amount of energy.

Adelie penguins travel at speed by 'porpoising'. Air is less dense than water, so it is more efficient to leap from one medium to the other and take advantage of both.

DEEP DIVERS

WHEN A HUNTING animal is limited by one gulp of air, speed is necessary to take it to where it is going quickly and to get it back safely. Several sea-birds, sea mammals and sea-going reptiles have this requirement when diving deep.

Sea-snakes pursue fish, particularly eels which are the right shape for a snake to eat, and may reach depths of 328ft (100m). They can stay down for up to 5 hours. Of the flying birds, the loon or great northern diver has been credited with pursuing prey at 200ft (61m) in Lake Superior and a guillemot was recorded at 240ft (73m) in the cod-rich waters off Newfoundland. In the North Sea, the crew of a submersible were startled to see a cormorant at considerable depth.

But the emperor penguin of the Antarctic, the largest of the penguins, is the deepest diving bird. It can stay below for up to 18 minutes and reach a depth of at least 870ft (265m). The slightly smaller king penguins of sub-Antarctic islands have been tracked down to 787ft (240m), although only half their dives on a fishing trip might be below 164ft (50m). In the food-rich waters of the Southern Ocean, their main prey is squid.

Hunting birds, with chicks to feed back on land, are out at sea for periods of 4-8 days. They must catch 6lb (2.5kg) of food for themselves and a further 7lb (3kg) for the chick each day. On every fishing trip, then, a bird must catch between 50-90 squid weighing 5-7oz (150-200g) each. With an average of 865 dives per excursion, this means that king penguins catch squid on fewer than 10 per cent of their dives.

Sperm whales go after bigger prizes - giant squid. In order to reach them, sperm whales must dive very deep, the deepest dives of any air-breathing animal. One whale, off South Africa, was credited with a dive that lasted 1 hour and 52 minutes. It was caught by a whaling ship and in its stomach were found two deep-water sharks that only live at the sea-bottom. The charts show the place to be 10,476ft (3,193m) deep.

Why sperm whales should go so deep is not clear, although it is thought that they are using a food resource that is not exploited by many other hunters. Seals, sea-lions, smaller-toothed whales, dolphins and a whole host of fast-swimming fishes skim off the bulk of the squid from the surface waters, while sperm whales dive deep below and avoid the competition.

Using their great, powerful tails they dive straight down at speeds of up to 558ft (170m) per minute. Bulls dive the deepest and longest, while cows level out at about 3,000ft (914m). They return to the surface just as fast, avoiding the 'bends' with the aid of specialised respiratory and circulation mechanisms that ensure there is no air in the blood when the whale is at depth.

There is also the suggestion that the spermaceti organ in the forehead has, in addition to being a sound lens, a secondary function. The organ is criss-crossed with a complicated plumbing system of blood vessels, sinuses and nasal passages, and it is filled with a special wax that melts at 84.2 degrees F (29 degrees C) precisely. The whale, it is thought, can melt or solidify the wax at will, thereby changing its density. This has the effect of making its body more or less buoyant, so the whale can control its ability to go down or rise up.

It works like this: at the surface, seawater is circulated to cool the wax, which shrinks and becomes more dense, causing the whale to sink. At the end of the dive, body heat generated by the muscles is carried by the blood system into the spermaceti organ, where it melts the wax. The head is then less dense than the water and the animal rises to the surface with the minimum effort. No matter how exhausted the animal becomes at the bottom, it is assured a safe journey to the surface - important after a long feeding excursion or a titanic struggle with a giant squid.

The cuttlefish undergoes amazing colour changes before it catches its prey. The shrimp is thought to be mesmerised by the constant changes of pattern. Two long tentacles are thrust rapidly from the ring of 8 arms and capture the prey. The tentacles pull the shrimp towards the bird-like beak at the centre of the arms. This tears into the shrimp's exoskeleton and extracts the flesh.

SHOOTING FROM THE HIP

SQUID, CUTTLEFISH AND octopuses are amazing creatures. They have a large brain and eyes like our own, and, quite literally, they wear their thoughts on their skin. In the skin of a cephalopod there are thousands of elastic-walled colour cells, which can be filled or drained of pigment in an instant. In fact, squid and cuttlefish are capable of the fastest changes of colour in the animal kingdom. And they put it to good use.

Cuttlefish are fond of shrimps and crabs. The approach is slow, the predator blending with its background, but on the final approach a remarkable thing happens. The cuttlefish strikes a pose, with the two of its eight short arms raised, whilst a fantastic, changing kaleidoscope of colours passes down its body. Moving patterns of zebra stripes, longitudinal and transverse bars, spots and blotches mesmerise the crustacean. It hasn't seen anything like this before. Then, at the last moment the cuttlefish strikes. Two long tentacles shoot out from the circle of arms. At their distal end are pads of suckers which grab the prey and draw it back to the mouth, where a horny beak pulverises the shell.

The body of the common cuttlefish is 16in (40cm) long and its tentacles extend to about half the length of its body. But imagine the snatching power of a giant squid with a body 20ft (6.1m) long and tentacles that stretch to 35ft (10.7m). Just such a creature was washed ashore alive at Thimble Tickle in 1878. It was the largest, authenticated giant squid known to science. The eyes were 18in (0.5m) across and the largest suckers on the ends of the tentacles were 4in (10cm) in diameter. It was truly a giant amongst giants.

Many predatory sea animals have a slow, stealthy approach ending with the sudden movement of some body part or other. The angler fishes, with enormous mouths, must gulp down their duped prey in an instant, some fish exhibiting the fastest movements in the sea. When a grouper opens its mouth, the inrush of water can be so great that, with very large specimens, even humans have been known to be sucked in. Some fish increase the odds of success by projecting their jaws forward. The deep-sea loose-jaws resemble living skeletons with disarticulated mouths that gulp at passing prey. The John Dory, the fish with St Peter's thumb-prints on its side, has protrusible jaws with which, in a split second, it can grab prey fish.

The dragonfly is an effective predator even as a youngster. The nymph stage is aquatic, and it one of the most voracious freshwater killers. Its secret, like the John Dory, is in its jaws. The creature possesses a 'mask' (so-called because it masks the mouthparts), which consists of a lower jaw hinged to an upper jaw tipped with movable hooks. The whole structure can be extended in front of the nymph's face and can capture anything from small fish to large tadpoles.

Frogs and toads do not extend their jaws to gain an advantage, rather they throw out their tongue. Most tongues are attached at the back of the mouth, but the frog or toad tongue is attached at the front. At rest, the top surface of the tongue is sticky while the underside is not. The speed with which it can use the weapon is phenomenal, beyond our normal perception and only visible to us with the help of high-speed cameras.

The frog sits and waits for an insect to settle. Triggered by the prey's

The chameleon can change its colour to match its background; it has eyes which can point in any direction, but which come together to focus on a potential target; and it has a tongue with a sticky tip which can be projected some distance from the body to capture prey. The capture is over in a split second.

movement, the amphibian opens its mouth and the tongue is thrown out to twice its resting length. The sticky upper surface becomes the underside and lands on top of the prey. The insect sticks to the tongue and, like a piece of elastic, the tongue flies back into the mouth. All we perceive is an audible click, the insect disappears, followed by the frog making swallowing movements. The snatch takes just one-fifteenth of a second.

The ultimate tongue, though, has to be that of the chameleon. Although the animal itself is sluggish and appears to move very deliberately, it is a very successful hunter. It spots prey with its pair of turret-shaped eyes, each of which can move independently of the other. While one is looking up, the other can be peering straight ahead or down, giving the chameleon the ability to look everywhere at once. When prey is spotted, both eyes swivel rapidly to focus on the same spot. The predator now has stereoscopic vision with which it can accurately pinpoint the target.

Without disturbing the victim, the chameleon opens its mouth slightly and the globular end of its pink tongue protrudes. In an instant, the prey disappears and the chameleon is chewing on its meal. Again, the action is so fast, we cannot see it. In a split second, the tongue is fired out of the mouth, extending to twice the length of the chameleon's own body. The prey adheres to the stick mucus at the tip, and, equally quickly, the tongue plus food is retracted back into the mouth. In this way, one of the slowest creatures on earth makes one of the fastest movements.

The tongue of frogs and toads is attached at the front of the mouth and can be thrown out to catch prey on the sticky tip. This common toad has caught a beetle larva. The action is over in an instant.

The cheetah must stalk an adult gazelle and approach unseen to within 88yds (80m) before starting the pursuit, which, on average, is over in 317yds (290m). A vulnerable gazelle fawn is chased from 547yds (500m) and is more likely to be caught after 208yds (190m). Overheated and exhausted, the cheetah often rests before eating. Lions, leopards and hyenas are liable to steal the kill.

As one of the hawkers, an aeshna dragonfly patrols its territory constantly like a flying hawk. With a longer wingspan and longer, thinner body than the darters, hawkers can close in on their insect prey at speeds exceeding 18mph (30km/h).

Cormorants rely on speed and surprise to pursue fish underwater. They use their webbed feet for propulsion. This double-crested cormorant in the Crystal River in Florida is preparing to dive.

Swallows, like swifts and martins, have sickle-shaped wings that enable them to pursue flying insects. They rarely land on the ground and even drink on the wing.

Wait
& Catch

7

Patience brings its rewards. Many predators have
discovered that instead of dashing about the
place, using up valuable energy and failing to catch
anything half the time, it is more productive if they just
wait until the prey comes to them. There are those that
sit tight, in one spot, and those that drift about,
sometimes aimlessly and sometimes with a purpose.
Some are camouflaged and go unrecognised, others
ensure that they are simply in the right
place at the right time.
Some of the simplest, multi-celled organisms on earth
have adopted a 'sit-and-wait' strategy, but their encounters with prey are more organised than one might
think. Over millions of years, even these relatively
simple creatures have perfected the art of
making things happen.
And although the more active hunters generally move
rapidly in pursuit of prey, there are times when it is
prudent to wait and watch. Pike, for example, will lie
motionless amongst the waterweeds waiting for a small
fish to swim past, and the mountain lion will hide
behind rocks waiting for a victim to come close.
Standing, sitting or lying quite still has proved to be an
excellent way for a hunter to catch a meal.

JEWELLED KILLERS

S<small>EA-ANEMONES SIT</small> on rocks, on pilings, on hermit crabs and on the seabed and wait for a meal to come their way. They are solitary, soft-bodied coelenterates (simple animals with a double skin). Although attached firmly to the substrate by a large, sucker-like base and seemingly blind and deaf, anemones are surprisingly aware of the world about them.

Contrary to popular belief, they do not simply wait for something to bump into them, for they can hear and smell their prey approaching and so are alert to launch an attack. At rest, the anemone tunes into a high frequency - about 55Hz or 55 cycles per second. The hair-like cilia which detect vibrations in the water are relatively short and might pick up fish movements or something similar. If, however, a favourite species of shrimp approaches, chemoreceptors detect the smell of the prey (in fact, the chitin-like sugars of the shrimp's shell) and the vibration detectors lengthen. This enables them to pick up vibrations at 5Hz, the frequency of the swimming movements of the shrimp. In this way,

The beadlet anemone appears just to sit and wait for a passing meal to blunder into it. In reality, it can detect the vibrations and smell of prey nearby and is ready to react ultra-quickly should it touch the anemone's deadly tentacles.

W O L V E S   I N   S H E E P S '   C L O T H I N G

S<small>ome</small> animals identify and locate concentrations of prey animals and just plonk themselves down in the middle of them. For very little effort they can just reach out and grab a meal. But the cheekiest method of hunting must be a form of behaviour known as aggressive mimicry. The predator is not camouflaged and does not use stealth, but pretends to be something innocuous or doing something that will not alarm the prey. Rats sometimes stroll nonchalantly towards their prey, only to spring an attack at the last minute. Zone-tailed hawks fly with vultures. Small mammals have nothing to fear from the large scavengers and they do not run away. The hawk is able to dart out from its cover and grab a victim. And one of the pipefish family - the trumpet fish - rides on the backs of parrot fish. The parrot fish are considered harmless to other small fishes for they browse on coral and the other reef fishes regard them with indifference. Any small fish that approaches, however, is in for a sad surprise. The trumpet fish slips down from its perch and grabs the prey.

the sea-anemone is alert at the moment it is brushed by the shrimp, and it can act immediately and immobilise the shrimp before it has time to escape.

Sea-anemones open slowly and their crown of tentacles wave about idly in the tide or current, but the moment prey touches predator, the movement is instantaneous. The tentacles curl around the food item, conduct it to the central mouth and it is swallowed. In less than a minute the sea-anemone has unfurled and is ready to catch again. Although they may resemble elegant undersea flowers, they are, in fact, voracious undersea predators.

CURTAINS OF DEATH

JELLYFISH ARE FREE-SWIMMING versions of sea-anemones. They float about in the ocean waiting for prey animals to blunder into the tentacles that hang below the bell. They can grow to immense sizes. The Arctic jellyfish is found in shallow bays in the North Atlantic, and one specimen was found in Massachusetts Bay in 1865 that was 7ft 6in (2.29m) in diameter and had tentacles hanging 120ft (36.6m) below the bell. This curtain of death could cover an area of 500yds (457m) square. A related species, the lion's mane jellyfish, reaches 1m across and has yellow tentacles up to 49ft (15m) long. Occasionally, 1/2-mile (800m) swarms are seen drifting towards the Norwegian coast, and the species prompted Sir Arthur Conan Doyle to employ its sting for criminal ends in the Sherlock Holmes' mystery *Adventures with the Lion's Mane.*

The lion's mane jellyfish drifts passively over the Great Barrier Reef. Its trailing tentacles, armed with miniature poisonous harpoons, are ready to catch passing fish. Some fish appear to be immune to the venom and seek safety

In reality lion's mane jellyfish are not that dangerous to man, but others are. Huge plagues of a red jellyfish sometimes make life a misery for holidaymakers in the Mediterranean. Shoals of 100,000 at a time have been seen drifting off holiday beaches along the Greek coast, and in 1987 Egyptian beaches were jammed with slicks of jellyfish 1m thick and 1km long, a phenomenon which has been blamed both on pollution and the reduction in numbers of sea turtles, but in reality has been going on for centuries. Jellyfish blooms were recorded over 100 years ago.

The business end of the jellyfish is its tentacles. The bell itself is more concerned with getting the jellyfish to where it wants to go and digesting any food its tentacles might catch. In the main a collision with prey is an accident, but some species arrange themselves so tnat an accident is more likely. One species swimming off the US Pacific coast drives itself up to the surface with contractions of its saucer-shaped bell until it reaches the surface. Then, it turns upside down and drifts slowly down trailing its sixty or so tentacles behind it. It is thought that by manoeuvring in this way, the jellyfish creates vortices in the water that sweep small organisms into the tentacles. Another species in the same waters swims a zig-zag course so that its tentacles sweep an area greater than the width of the bell and increases the chances of snarling prey.

Some jellyfish follow the daily vertical migration of plankton and small fish. At night they rise to the surface and by day they sink to the depths. But jellyfish cannot adjust their buoyancy and so they must actively swim all the way. One Mediterranean species, just $1^1/2$in across, swims a daily vertical round trip of 3,600ft, the equivalent of a man swimming 33 miles a day every day.

COMBS AND GOOSEBERRIES

RELATED TO THE JELLYFISH, comb jellies and sea gooseberries are technically known as ctenophores. They are a half-way stage between the round-shaped jellyfish and sea-anemones and the bilaterally symmetrical flatworms. They have transparent bodies and float about with the zooplankton, their tentacles trailing like fishing lines.

Comb jellies are tiny, 4cm-long, transparent barrels which propel themselves through the water with the help of rows of moving hairs (cilia). They trail 50cm-long, adhesive tentacles with lateral filaments containing adhesive cells that can stick to prey that might blunder into them. Pipefish, which are a similar size to the comb jelly, have been seen to be 'played' until exhausted.

Sea gooseberries live near the surface and tend to bump into prey. A sense organ near the mouth detects when a contact is made and the body immediately contorts. The body shortens, the gut widens, and the prey is swept into the mouth by the sudden inrush of water. The mouth is then closed and the unfortunate victim trapped.

Some comb jellies have 'lasso' cells. These burst on contact, releasing a lasso to capture small prey organisms such as rotifers.

SAILORS AND MEN-OF-WAR

TRAILING BENEATH its purple-coloured, balloon-like float, the Portuguese man-of-war has millions of stinging cells available to catch its prey, usually small fish which collide with the tentacles.

The Portuguese man-of-war is a colonial hydroid and consists of several different types of polyps, known as 'persons', that join together for the greater good of the co-operative. Some specialise in digestion, others in reproduction, floating or catching food. The 10-30cm-long float, which is frilled along the top, is filled with gas secreted by a special gland. Periodically the float is collapsed to first one side and then the other to moisten it and to protect the delicate membrane from drying out. When inflated, it sits on the surface of the sea, where it is blown about the ocean by the wind. Under certain conditions hundreds of men-of-war are blown together in huge rafts.

The flattened, frilled part of the bladder is angled at 45 degrees, which means that the creature actually sails. Men-of-war in the northern hemisphere have their sails set differently from those in the southern hemisphere, some being right-handed and others left-handed. The vast array of tentacles below acts as a drogue or sea anchor, helping to steer a course at a set angle to the wind. If caught in westerlies, the sail aligns south-west to north-east, the tentacles trail to the north-west, and the creature makes progress towards the south-east. By angling the sail, the Portuguese man-of-war avoids being blown into areas of doldrums like the Sargasso Sea.

The pink-and-blue curtain of tentacles can reach down 30ft or more below the float and they catch fish as large as mackerel. Once caught and paralysed by the 'prey catching persons', the prey is hoisted up to the mouth, where the 'digestion persons' deal with it and distribute the nutrients to the entire colony.

Floating at the surface and supported by a bladder of gas, the Portuguese man-of-war is a colony of individuals each doing a particular job; there are those that catch food, others that digest it, some to keep the colony afloat, and yet others that look after reproduction. The food catchers have tentacles trailing 30ft (10m) below the bladder and they can deliver a toxin chemically similar to the venom of a cobra.

A relative of the Portuguese man-of-war is the by-the-wind sailor, and it too sails in the wind. Instead of a single, large, gas-filled bladder, the by-the-wind sailor has a 10cm-diameter, circular disc of gas-filled chambers which keeps it afloat. Like the man-of-war, the creature is a colonial one with reproductive persons surrounding the central mouth below the disc, and stinging persons fringing the disc, but its most interesting feature is the very obvious 'sail' on top of the disc. It is also angled so that the colony sails like a yacht, and flotillas of by-the-wind sailors all travel together in the same direction.

Floating along with them are often purple sea-snails. These voracious snails float on a raft of bubbles and feed on by-the-wind sailors. They eat all the soft parts, leaving the circular disc to which they sometimes attach their eggs.

MINIATURE KILLER HARPOONS

ALL THE SEA-ANEMONES, coral polyps, jellyfish and other related coelenterates, like box jellies, comb jellies and Portuguese men-of-war, kill in the same way - with stinging cells known as nematocysts. There are rows of nematocysts on the tentacles. Each venom-filled cell contains a coiled, barbed thread, which resembles the finger of a rubber glove pushed in. The cell is capped with a lid and has a trigger on the outside. The prey blunders into the tentacles, pushes against the triggers of many nematocysts and each of them discharges like a miniature harpoon. The lid flies open, the coiled barbs evert and shoot out, entering the flesh of the clumsy victim. The discharge is so rapid that the barb leaves the cell at 2m per second with an acceleration of 40,000 times the force of gravity, about

10,000 times that experienced by astronauts at take-off. The harpooning is over in three-thousandths of a second, making it the fastest cellular process in nature.

Even though they are microscopic in size, the stinging cells of some jellyfish and Portuguese men-of-war are so strong that they can penetrate a rubber glove and human skin. A single jelly might produce several different poisons. One poison stops the heart of the victim, another disrupts the blood system by destroying red blood cells, and a third attacks the brain. The poison is a powerful neurotoxin related to that produced by the king cobra, but it takes 24,000 nematocysts to make a milligram.

Once thought to be the larvae of barnacle geese, the goose barnacle catches food in its feet. It can get about if it is attached to drift-wood, slow-swimming turtles or whales. Otherwise the barnacle is restricted to a sessile life.

Although the Portuguese man-of-war is considered dangerous to man, few deaths have occurred directly from it stinging. Usually, a bather is stung over the body and drowns accidentally. The sea-wasp, however, **is** deadly. It is one of the box jellies with a small bell about 10in across and 66ft-long tentacles. It is the most dangerous sea creature known for it can kill a person in just 3-8 minutes.

Some creatures have come to terms with the toxic tentacles of 'jellyfish' and sea-anemones and use them as weapons. The blanket octopus, for instance, snips off manageable pieces of Portuguese man-of-war tentacles and uses them to sting prey such as shrimps. Similarly, the boxer crab grabs a chunk of sea-anemone in each claw and brandishes them like boxing gloves.

F<small>ILTER</small> FEEDERS

M<small>ANY UNDERSEA CREATURES</small> filter the water for food and, like the sea-anemones and corals, might be considered stationary hunters. They hijack tiny zooplankton, often aided by minute nets that sieve the water. Barnacles, for instance, are tiny shrimps encased in calcareous houses. There are two main types - the stalked goose barnacle, which is found on drifting wood and pilings, and the sessile acorn barnacle, which lies flat against rocks. The barnacle has been described as 'a crustacean standing on its head and kicking food into its mouth with its feet' - and that, in a nutshell, is precisely what it is. The barnacle lies on its back in its shell, which is attached to the rock with a remarkable glue twice as strong as epoxy resins. Through the opening in the top it kicks its 6 legs in the air, the legs opening and closing at the rate of 140 times a minute. The legs are 'hairy' and trap animals from the plankton. Some do not wait about on rocks but take a free ride on other larger animals. There are species that specialise in attaching themselves to sea turtles, and others that prefer the fins of whales and dolphins. They are not parasites, for they do no harm to their host, which is simply a convenient platform from which the barnacles can 'fish'.

ROCKS THAT BITE

CAMOUFLAGE ENABLES a waiting predator to become effectively 'invisible' and be ready to surprise an unwary passer-by. In the sea, fish that frequent the seabed ambush their prey in this way. The venomous stone fish resembles, as its name suggests, weed-covered coral, rocks or stones, and its outline only becomes apparent to the casual observer if the eyes can be picked out first. Similarly, sluggish, bottom-dwelling scorpion fish and angler fish have flaps, projections and modified spines that give them the appearance of weed-encrusted rocks or bottom sediments. The angler fish even has a weed-like skirt around its entire body which disguises it on the rough sea-floor on which it sits. If a small fish should venture near the large, wide mouth, it opens in a flash and the prey is drawn in with the inrush of water.

The creature with one of the biggest gulps must be the angel shark, a flattened, bottom-living shark that waits hidden in sand or mud. Unlike other sharks, it relies less on sophisticated electric, smell and vibration senses to detect its prey; rather, it is responsive to visual movements. If a fish swims by, the angel shark lifts itself from the bottom, opens its gigantic mouth, sucks the prey in and returns once more to rest on the seabed.

Another type of bottom-living shark - the wobbegongs of Australian waters - resembles a shaggy, fringed carpet with weed-like tufts of skin that break up the outline of the head. There are several species and, unlike other sharks which tend to be uniformly grey or brown above and white below, they are characterised by the intricate patterns of spots, stripes and blotches that make them difficult to see on the sea-floor or amongst corals or weeds on which they lie motionless. The mouth is filled with row upon row of needle-like teeth with which they seize small fishes, shrimps, crabs and sea-urchins, and there are even some reports of larger species (they grow up to 10ft long) attacking people.

Not all mimics sit on the bottom. The Sargassum angler fish has the colour, pattern and texture of floating sargassum weed into which it all but disappears. Lest a quivering fin might give it away, the fish has modified pectoral fins with which it holds tight to sargassum fronds and drifts imperceptibly with the weed.

Some fish, though cryptically coloured and blending in somewhat to their background, simply hide in rocks and crevices ready to dart out and grab unsuspecting prey. The most common are the moray eels that lurk in rock and coral crevices waiting to hijack fish, crabs and other small marine creatures. The largest are the groupers that live a solitary existence in caverns and holes, emerging only to snatch a passing fish. They can grow to immense sizes, up to 8ft (2.4m) long, and weigh nearly half a tonne. They tend to position themselves low in the water. The prey is then silhouetted against the bright surface waters above and easy to see.

DEADLY FLOWERS

CRAB SPIDERS SIT in flowers and mimic the colour and patterns to such a degree that they are, to our eyes at least, almost invisible. Wearing this cloak of anonymity, they are able to intercept their prey. Instead of spinning a web like orb weavers or chasing after prey like wolf spiders, crab spiders sit motionless amongst the petals and anthers of insect-pollinated flowers and wait for insects, such as butterflies and hoverflies, to visit.

Matching its flowering background, the crab spider appears invisible to a visiting pollinator.

When an insect alights, the spider grabs its head and bites into its mouth parts, reversing the normal flow of nutrients, and sucks out the body fluids. Desiccated butterflies are often left resting on the flower, much to the surprise of any butterfly collector about to pounce on his prize specimen only to find that it does not try to escape.

The cryptic coloration is important. In an experiment with dandelion flowers, a scientist once placed yellow pebbles on half the flowers and black pebbles on the rest. Insects were very reluctant to visit the flowers with the conspicuous black pebbles, indicating that without the flower-matching colours a crab spider would have a very lean time indeed.

Flowers, of course, do not last very long and so, when its flower is spent, the spider moves to another bloom and can even adjust its colour to match its new home. There is, however, a curious postscript to the crab spider story. Insects see different wavelengths of light than we do, and are able to see ultraviolet light reflected from flowers. Significantly, flowers look very different when viewed at these wavelengths. Striped nectar guides, like airport runway landing lights, show pollinators the fast way to the reservoirs of nectar, and crab spiders show up quite clearly. In theory, then, insects should be able to see the spiders. It is a mystery why they don't avoid them.

In the tropics, there are colourful species of praying mantis that mimic the flowers on which they sit. These are the flower mantids, and although they are much larger than the crab spiders, they are only visible when they move. One of the most beautiful is the so-called devil's flower, an African mantid with red-and-white legs. White orchids in South-East Asia have their own deadly orchid mantids that resemble white petals.

Praying mantids also mimic leaves and sticks, and they get their name from the prayer-like attitude of their first pair of hinged, grasping limbs that can extend forwards instantly in one-twentieth of second to snatch a meal. They have insatiable appetites and are skilled predators. One specimen was seen to snatch and eat 10 cockroaches in a space of only 3 hours. Mantids come in all shapes and sizes, some as large as $6^{1}/_{2}$in (16.6cm) long, and catch small frogs and lizards.

Perhaps the most unlikely predators to lie in wait on a branch are the larval stages of moths. The Hawaiian looper caterpillar, along with 20 related species, is a killer caterpillar. It rests on a leaf or stem, grasping it with its rear suckers, and extends itself out at an angle, looking to all the world like a straight, green twig. If, however, a fly should come close and touch sensitive hairs on its back, the caterpillar bends rapidly and seizes the prey in its grasping forelegs. With the victim firmly caught, it straightens out once more and devours the prize.

A CATERPILLAR IN THE ANTS' DEN

LARGE, BLUE CATERPILLARS seek out the nests of red ants and contrive to place themselves amongst an ample supply of food on which they fatten up for a winter-long period of pupation.

In the autumn in Europe, the large, blue caterpillar reaches a stage where it changes from its previous herbivorous diet to a carnivorous one. It stops eating the thyme leaves on which it has been feasting for several weeks, climbs down from the plant and searches for a particular species of red ant. Having found one, it rears up and produces a drop of honey from a special gland in its abdomen. The ant is pacified; normally it would attack the caterpillar and capture it for the colony's larder. Instead, it picks it up and carries it carefully back into the heart of the ants' nest. Likewise, the rest of the colony does not tear the caterpillar to pieces. More honey secretions and the release of a special smell or pheromone appeases the ants and they accept the caterpillar. They 'milk' it, palpating the honey gland in order to obtain further supplies. Safe and snug in the nest, the caterpillar repays its hosts by gobbling up their larvae.

The caterpillar continues to live in the nest, eating the ant larvae and pupae, for 5 or 6 weeks and then changes into the pupa or chrysalis. At this stage it continues to placate its ant hosts by producing more sugar solutions, pheromones and rasping sounds. The sounds are created by scratching the abdomen on the wall of the pupal case. It mimics 'ant talk', a particularly clever thing for a butterfly to do.

SURROUNDED WITH FOOD

WITH HUNDREDS OF greenfly or blackfly packed tightly on to a flower bud, a prime position for any insect predator might be right there in the midst of them, and that is precisely where the hungry larvae and adults of certain flies and beetles contrive to be.

The parent predators give their offspring a good start in life by depositing their eggs on the right plants. Ladybirds like aphids and they place their eggs on the undersides of leaves close to aphid colonies. When the slate-blue larvae hatch out, they head upwards, for up is where the flowers and the aphids are. During their 3 weeks of life, the larvae devour hundreds of aphids, piercing the skins and sucking them dry. Then they pupate and re-emerge as adult beetles, which also feed on aphids.

The small, soft-bodied, slug-like larva of the hover fly is also a predator of

The hoverfly is the gardener's friend. A hoverfly parent deposits her eggs close to food, and so the emerging larvae need not travel far to be surrounded by their favourite delicacy - aphids.

aphids. Like the ladybird, the egg from which it emerged was deposited close to aphids. It can detect light but has poor eyesight and, therefore, must find its prey by smell. Moving across a leaf on its flattened underside, it glides along on saliva. It grabs an aphid with its mouth hooks and rears up, holding the unfortunate fly high in the air. All the soft parts inside the prey are sucked out, leaving the shrivelled exoskeleton behind. And having scoffed one aphid, it goes on to eat many, many more before pupating and changing, by metamorphosis, into the nectar-sipping adult.

Lacewings, both adult and larvae, attack aphids, and the larvae of certain species of green lacewings, having finished their meal, show a curious piece of behaviour: they take the skin of their victim and place it on their back. The debris seems to function as a shield against predators, but not all lacewings have them. By the time an individual has consumed its 100 or so aphids, it has a considerable load to carry. After pupation adult green lacewings discontinue the debris-carrying habit, but their adult brown lacewing cousins might go on

to consume an average of 315 aphids during their short lifetime. Lacewings, hover flies and ladybirds are clearly gardeners' friends and are important insects in the biological control of pests.

Larger animals also contrive to surround themselves with their food supply. The spiny moloch lizard sits beside ant trails licking up to 20-30 per minute and consumes, in an average meal, about 1,800 ants. Aardvarks, aardwolfs and bat-eared foxes in Africa, ant-eaters in South America and echidnas in Australia have to work a little harder. They are all great consumers of ants or termites (which are not related to ants but are colonial cockroaches), but they must dig into nests until they reach their insect bonanza.

The giant ant-eater has powerful forelimbs and tough, digging claws that can tear into the nests of ants. It has, however, a long, delicate snout and, therefore, avoids the nests of termites, leaf-cutting ants and army ants which have large-jawed soldiers that could inflict painful bites. Colonies are found by smell (in experiments, they can detect an odour four-thousandths of the natural odour at

Spraying garden plants with insecticides not only kills the pests, but also the pest killers. Natural pest control has ladybird larvae feeding on aphids; and the more aphids, the more ladybirds to reduce their numbers.

The curiously-shaped aardvark gets right in amongst its food. It has a passion for termites and ants, and has large and powerful digging claws to break into their nests. A worm-like, 8in (20cm) long tongue can be stretched double its length in order to probe every nook and cranny for food.

an ants' nest) and excavated with the large claws, but the ant-eater only feeds for a short time, probably no more than a minute, during which it eats about 140 ants. The digging does not destroy the ants' nest and the cropping is well short of over-exploiting the resource. So, in order to gain a fair day's food, the ant-eater visits many different nests in its home range, taking a little from each.

The ants are extracted by the tongue, which can be 24in (60cm) long. Muscles regulating the movement of the tongue are attached to the breastbone and can push and pull the tongue in and out a remarkable 150 times a minute. Huge amounts of thick saliva coat the tongue and trap the ants. In the mouth they are scrunched first against the nobbly roof of the mouth and cheeks and then squeezed in the muscular stomach. The animal must visit a hundred or so nests to satisfy its daily nutritional requirement.

DANGER IN THE DARK

IN THE ENORMOUS, cathedral-like caves of Malaysia, some of the largest caves in the world, there exists an extraordinary collection of animals that depend on cave swiflets that nest and roost in the caves by night and bats that roost there by day. The swiftlets are those responsible for making the famous saliva-cut nests which are the main ingredient in birds' nest soup, and their journeys in and out of the caves are fraught with dangers. Waiting on the cave walls are cave racer snakes, ready to pluck swiftlets or bats from mid-air, and in the bat guano heaps below, a veritable house of horrors awaits the unfortunate flyer forced to ditch on the cave floor.

The snakes are well able to navigate in the dark. They follow well-worn, rippled ribbons of polished guano into the deep recesses of the caves, and can climb the walls to reach swiftlet nests, where they grab eggs or chicks. More unexpectedly, they coil around stalactites, stalagmites and rocky projections at narrow points in the cave passages, places where traffic flow is restricted and flying animals must slow their flight. The snakes hang out into the void with mouth agape and snatch at anything that comes close. It is thought that air-pressure waves from the flapping wings are detected by the snakes, although the snakes have been heard to make mewing sounds - an unusual thing for a snake to do - which might have something to do with echolocation, a common way in which cave animals find prey.

The cave are also home to hunting spiders, which, like many other troglodytes, are blind. They run about with their first pair of legs, which are covered with sensory hairs, held out in front like antennae. With these they can detect the movements of the smaller cave crickets.

The cave crickets themselves grow to monster proportions, and one of the most spectacular predators is a giant with huge legs and muscular jaws that can tear a cave swiftlet chick apart, even in the nest high above the cave floor. One specimen has been seen to take a swiftlet egg in its jaws and smash it against the rock and eat it.

In the cave streams that gouge rills and ridges between the bat dung, cave crabs and giant toads battle for injured fledglings. Two crabs might tear a chick in half. A related species, deep in the caves, has lost all pigment, has reduced eyes and possesses long legs with which it can crawl about the caves like an amphibious spider. Long-legged centipedes, multi-legged, cave earwigs and shimmering golden cockroaches complete the horrible picture.

Outside, the entrances of the caves are patrolled by bat hawks, dark pere-

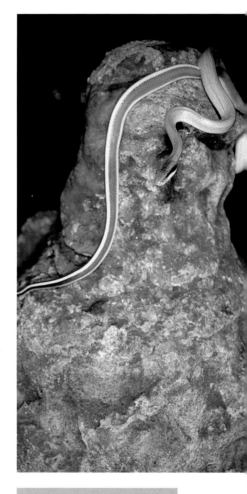

In the dark inner passages of a Sarawak cavern, cave racer snakes hang from stalagmites and stalactites ready to grab bats and cave swiftlets as they fly past. The victims are caught in mid-air.

grine-sized raptors that take advantage of the comings and goings at dawn and dusk. They too wait and watch, placing themselves at a point of plenty, ready to take advantage of the superabundance of prey. At dawn, the swiftlets leave en masse to feed by day and the bats return to roost. At dusk, it is the reverse, and the bat hawks are ready to pounce. They swoop in at an angle across the cave mouth and tear through the emerging and returning flocks. Every morning and evening there is pandemonium as bats and swiftlets, both pursued by hawks, change shifts. At twilight the bats stream out and the swiftlets, diving a spiral from a great height to avoid the waiting predators, fly in. If it were not for the bats and the birds, this remarkable community would not exist. They collect from the surrounding forest and provide enough food to support a cave floor fauna that is most likely larger than that on the floor of the forest itself.

FISHING FOR SALMON

BEING IN THE right place at the right time is the prerogative of two of America's well-known animals - the grizzly bear and the bald eagle - and they time their arrival to the movements of fish. Grizzlies, living along the Pacific coast of North America, head for key rivers, such as Canada's Mackenzie River, with the view to catching choice salmon. Pacific salmon, like their relatives in other parts of the world, return to their home river to spawn. A clock could almost be set to their arrival, with different species of fish entering the rivers at different times of the year. In July, the sockeye salmon enter the rivers of Alaska and British Columbia. They congregate in huge numbers in the estuaries, where they fall prey to killer whales and seals, before making the perilous journey up-river to the salmon redds at the head of the river, where they deposit their eggs and milt. Waiting for them, along the river-bank, are not only the nets and lines of fishermen and anglers, but also the massed claws of countless grizzlies.

Grizzly bears would not normally accept other bears to be in such close proximity, but with the expected food boom they are slightly more tolerant of each other. Fights do break out as the grizzlies line up at convenient cataracts. They jostle one another for the best positions on rocks in mid-stream, the more mature bears gaining the prime sites, and they wait for the salmon to run. At rapids and low waterfalls, the salmon must fight hard to swim up and over the white water, and it is here that they are most vulnerable.

With a lightning swipe of the forepaw a grizzly can hook a salmon as it leaps clear of the water or scoop one out of the shallows. Some bears simply stand in the water at the top of the rapids and wait for the fish to, quite literally, jump into their mouth.

With the run complete and with full bellies, the bears head for the hills and for winter hibernation. The surviving salmon reach their spawning grounds, where many die, exhausted by the supreme effort of procreation. Some live on, returning to the sea, to spawn another day, but on the return journey there is another gauntlet to run.

In the pine trees bordering the Chilkat River, large numbers of bald eagles begin to gather. They are on their migration south to warmer climes, but they stop off for one last feast. In the river, dead, dying and exhausted salmon are washed down-river, easy pickings for the assembled predators. The eagles swoop in and snatch salmon from the shallows, the wriggling fish impaled on the eagle's powerful talons. Bears, raccoons and foxes join the easy hunt. It is the last of the summer food and a final opportunity to stock up before winter.

Bald eagles, on their way south for the winter, gather in the Chalkut Valley for a fish bonanza. Dead and dying salmon, returning from their breeding grounds, can be plucked with little effort from the shallows and taken to a perch to be consumed.

Each year, grizzly bears arrive at cataracts on Alaska's major river, where they wait for the salmon to pass through on their way to the redds in the headwaters. The salmon are plump and full of eggs and milt. Their struggles up the foaming waters makes catching them easy for the bears. Some bears just open their mouths and the salmon, quite literally, jump right in. The superabundance of food helps the bears put on extra fat for the winter.

A coral reef is made up of millions of tiny, sea-anemone-like coral polyps, each set in its own lime cup. At night, they extend their tentacles and catch tiny, floating marine organisms.

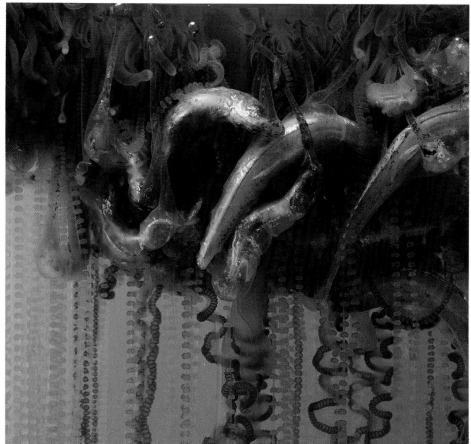

Having captured a fish, the tentacles of the Portuguese man-of-war contract and haul the victim towards the individuals in the colony that take on the role of digestion.

Jellyfish are not confined to tropical seas. Some, like this lion's mane, float northwards on the Gulf Stream to the Norwegian coast.

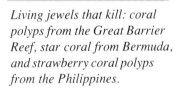

Living jewels that kill: coral polyps from the Great Barrier Reef, star coral from Bermuda, and strawberry coral polyps from the Philippines.

The European praying mantis stands quite motionless and waits patiently for an insect to come close. This individual has surprised a large white butterfly. Using its extendable, grasping forelegs, it has snatched the insect from its landing place and is slowly nibbling away at the body.

A bee and a fly, visiting flower heads to collect nectar or pollen, are seized by waiting crab spiders. The wait-and-catch predators are disguised in such a way that they blend in with the flowers in which they are hiding.

The giant ant-eater of South America is fond of large ground-living ants. It has a long, narrow snout containing a tongue with tiny spines covered in sticky saliva. Sharp claws help it enter ants' nests, but it avoids ants and termites with dangerous jaws that fight back.

The tamandua or collared ant-eater digs for termites and ants which it detects by their scent. It avoids ants which have chemical weapons. The ant-eater itself has its own special odour that has given it the reputation of being a bit of a 'stinker'.

Pangolins are found in Africa and Asia. They are nocturnal and eat ants and termites. Their bodies are covered with horny, overlapping scales. They have powerful claws with which they dig into nests. Cape pangolins (in picture) prefer termites, but when ousted by aardvarks they switch reluctantly to ants.

The echidna or spiny ant-eater of Australia is an egg-laying mammal or monotreme that, like the placental ant-eaters, has taken to specialising in ant-eating - a process known as 'convergent evolution' in which two unrelated animals in the same circumstances have solved the same problem in the same way.

Lined up in the expectation of a feast, grizzly bears in the Katriai National Park, Alaska, wait in the river for the salmon to run. The fish are either hooked with a deft swipe of the forepaw or caught in the mouth. The flesh is stripped off and the backbone discarded. Bears are usually solitary animals, but with such a concentration of food they tolerate each other's presence.

Pluck, Mystery, Conflict and Legend

8

Some predators take on quite formidable foe. Using speed, cunning and sheer tenacity to outwit and out-manoeuvre animals that are far larger and much more dangerous than themselves, these 'David and Goliath' encounters end up with the smaller animal gaining a meal.

Their pluck, however, can get them into trouble, and some persistent predators have come into conflict with people.

These man-animal clashes inevitably give rise to exaggerated stories of a predator's ability to kill and its danger to man. It is as if we need to be frightened by wild predators, a primeval throwback to a time when we had a closer affinity to nature and the prospect of being eaten alive was a real one. In people's minds, some predators have been transformed into 'monsters', the stories based not on facts but on tales handed down from generation to generation, the stuff of myths and legends, Unfortunately, just like the witch-hunts of the recent past, wild hunters are killed mindlessly, found guilty of crimes against humanity that, in reality, they have not committed. And no one thought to check until modern science had revealed that all is not what it seems.

PLAYING WITH SNAKES

THE ICHNEUMON MONGOOSE preys on cobras. They are snakes with such a powerful venom they could kill an unwary mongoose with one bite. The mongoose relies on speed, agility and the coarse fur which can be fluffed up to protect it somewhat from the snake's strikes. Its strategy is to tire the snake; then it can overpower it. It does this by launching mock attacks, dodging this way and that, careful to keep itself just out of reach. It repeatedly attacks, dancing out of range and making the snake strike at the air. Gradually the snake slows and its counter-attacks become less accurate. Exhausted and defenceless the snake is ready for the coup de grâce, and the mongoose dispatches it with a fatal bite, delivered by razor-sharp teeth, to the back of the neck.

QUITE A MOUTHFUL

SNAKES NEED NOT EAT very often. Most require little more than their own body weight each year and can fast for long periods. An Indian python was reported to eat nothing for 21 weeks and lost only 10 per cent of its body weight, while a reticulated python survived for a year and a half without a meal. But when they do eat, the food can be exceptionally large.

A snake is able to dislocate its jaws and swallow victims which have a greater width than the snake itself. This rock python has grabbed an impala, squeezed it to death by throwing coils of its body around it, and is about to swallow it whole.

SURPLUS KILLERS

Foxes, polecats and mink slaughter prey seemingly without reason. A fox in a hen-house appears to kill for the sake of killing, wiping out far more chickens than it could possible eat. But it is not the fault of the fox if it suddenly finds itself surrounded by prey. People have concentrated prey animals, like hens in a hen-house, in abnormally high numbers. The predatory impulse of a fox that gains entry is triggered every time the frightened birds flap and the fox will not stop killing until the stimulus has ceased. Undisturbed, the fox will take the spoils of its night's work and bury the carcasses nearby for future consumption. Lions do the same with cattle and wolves with sheep. Normally prey is so elusive that the opportunity to take advantage of a sudden superabundance of food is more than a predator can resist, and it will exploit the resource as best it can, a phenomenon known as 'surplus killing'.

All snakes have jaws that disarticulate, an adaptation to the fact that their body shape is basically long and narrow, and, without limbs or cutting teeth, they are not able to cut or break up food; instead, they swallow it whole. A large python might tackle prey the size of a wild pig or an antelope. It first catches the animal in its jaws and then crushes it to death. It wraps coils of its muscular body around the victim and slowly squeezes the life out of it. In reality, the snake cannot crush the bones, more it prevents the prey from breathing. The entire process is a reflex action, the snake responding to the movements of its victim. When it is deemed to be dead, the snake loosens its hold and swallows the prey head first.

The process of swallowing prey wider than itself has been solved by snakes in an ingenious way. The backward-pointing teeth prevent the prey from slipping forwards, and there are teeth top and bottom. The 6 upper jawbones are joined to the skull only by muscles and ligaments and can be moved independently of each other, and the two halves of the lower jaw are also not fused together. As the prey enters the mouth, the bones with teeth 'walk' the prey, moving alternately, first one side then the other. On reaching the oesophagus, the first section of gut after the mouth, the snake contorts its neck into an S-shape and pushes the carcass down into the stomach. There is no shoulder (pectoral) girdle or breastbone (sternum) to restrict the passage and the ribs expand. The skin can be stretched considerably without ripping.

Life-and-death struggles are often reported when large, constricting snakes attempt to eat more than they bargained for, particularly crocodiles and alligators. The inevitable outcome, however, is a win for the snake. A 23ft-long African Rock python was killed by hunters and opened up only to reveal a 5ft-long Nile crocodile in its stomach. A 26ft-long anaconda in eastern Brazil contained a similar-sized alligator. And a large Indian python was credited with eating a fully-grown leopard.

In zoos, constricting snakes have been seen to choke down the most extraordinary-sized meals. There is the tale told by German zoo-keeper Carl Hagenbeck of a 25ft (7.5m) reticulated python from Borneo being offered a 28lb male goat and then a few hours later a 39lb goat. Each was swallowed in about half an hour. A week later the zoo's female rock goat died, the horns were cut off and the carcass, weighing 74lb, was offered to the same snake. It immediately grabbed it and began to swallow. Hagenbeck, thinking that this was an amazing feat, sent for a photographer, but the flash frightened the snake and it regurgitated the entire goat in less than half a minute.

For the larger specimens, man can be on the snake's menu. Reports in newspapers in November 1977 tell of the body of a 45-year-old man who was cut from the stomach of an 18ft-long Indian python killed by villagers in Indonesia. The alarm was sounded when the villagers found the snake attacking a second person. And in July 1979 near Rocinha in Brazil, a fisherman was attending his nets when he was seized by an anaconda estimated to be 2ft in diameter. A day later, the villagers found the remains of his body washed ashore. His chest had been crushed.

EGG EATER

THE EGG-EATING SNAKE is equipped to crush not people but eggs; and it can deal with eggs twice the diameter of its body. Like all snakes, the egg-eating snake is able to disarticulate its jaws, but its mouth is wider, has smaller teeth and a larger gape, and is even more flexible than in other snakes. It can open its mouth to four times its resting size and swallow an egg whole.

At first, the egg is seized in the mouth, which, quite literally, stretches over the egg. Very slowly it moves down the gullet. The snake is still able to breathe for its windpipe can be pushed in and out of its mouth while feeding, the walls being strengthened with cartilage to prevent them collapsing. The egg is broken in the gullet. Strong muscles in the neck contract and spines on the neck vertebrae push down into the gullet and pierce the egg. The contents of the egg are digested while the egg shell is regurgitated.

PLUCKY PREDATORS

THE FISHER DOES not go fishing as its name suggests; rather, its name comes from the Old English 'fiche', meaning polecat, and it is one of the mustelids, a group of small, predatory animals with a characteristic anal gland that produces musk. The fisher is one of the martens, but it differs from its relatives by specialising in hunting the porcupine, probably one of the most extraordinarily difficult animals to catch. Porcupines have sharp quills all over the back, which they can erect as a defence. Other martens dispatch their prey with a firm bite to the back of the neck, but this is clearly denied the fisher. Instead, it must make repeated attacks at the porcupine, attempting to bite its unprotected face. The porcupine tries to keep its back to its attacker and so the task of outmanoeuvring it is long and hard. The fisher may take half an hour or more to land enough bites to disable the prey, but once victorious, the fisher has enough food to last it a couple of weeks.

Other mustelids include the weasel, stoat and polecat, all small but plucky predators well able to tackle prey, such as full-grown buck rabbits, much bigger than themselves, and, unlike the larger carnivores, they do their catching alone. If food is scarce, however, the weasel family are not averse to scavenging. Pine

The stoat, hunting alone and without help, sometimes tackles prey much larger than itself, including a fully grown rabbit.

martens find the carrion, such as elk and reindeer, left by larger predators by following their tracks, a behaviour known as 'parasitic tracking'.

The wolverine of northern lands is one of the largest mustelids, but it too tackles prey much larger and more powerful than itself. Its skill is demonstrated in winter, when thick snow covers the ground. Reindeer are a favourite food, for a large specimen will keep a wolverine well-stocked for several months. In summer, reindeer have the advantage and can run away, but in winter, their feet, though splayed to walk on crusty snow, sink deeper into soft snow than does the wolverine's broad, flat feet. The wolverine outruns the reindeer and leaps on to its back, sinking its teeth and claws into the back of its neck. And there it stays until the reindeer is exhausted and topples over. With powerful jaws, the wolverine dismembers the carcass and buries pieces around the forest. The freezing temperatures preserve the meat and the wolverine has only to remember where it left its caches to survive without hunting for a long while. It is this habit of storing food that earned the wolverine its common name of glutton. And if it cannot find prey, its ultra-sensitive nose directs it to the carcass left by a lynx or wolf. In a contest for carrion the wolverine wins hands down. In North America, the wolverine has been seen to compete successfully with 3 coyotes, another saw off a black bear, and in California 2 mountain lions abandoned their prey when a wolverine appeared.

SCANDINAVIAN MYSTERY

IT IS A HARSH LIFE in the Arctic, for animals and humans alike. The Lapps tend their huge herds of reindeer, wary of predators lest they steal animals from under their noses. Wolves are shot on sight and golden eagles are viewed with suspicion. Indeed, golden eagles were dubbed the villains in an Arctic mystery which was only recently solved.

The problem was that the Lapps were losing many of their new-born reindeer. The killer was unknown, but there were no dead carcasses to be seen. The killer, it was thought, must have swooped in from the skies, snatched a calf and carried it away to a safe distance to eat. The only large, aerial predator capable of doing such a thing was thought to be the golden eagle and an open season was declared on the birds. Many eagles were shot and conservationists became worried that the birds were in danger of becoming locally extinct. But something was not right. It was thought unlikely that eagles would take so many reindeer calves. They normally rely on smaller fare. So the scientists were called in and they set out to attempt to unravel the mystery.

Their first plan was to attach radio-collars to the new-born reindeer. Any calf that was removed by a predator could be tracked down and the predator caught red-handed, or so the theory went. The scientists watched and waited. The radio-collars were special ones that only switched on when a sensor inside detected lack of movement, that is, when the reindeer was dead. They did not have to wait long. Signals began to be transmitted and the scientists set off in pursuit. But they were in for a surprise, for when they approached the area the signal would disappear. This went on for some time until a researcher stumbled upon a radio-collar. It was buried in the earth along with a half-eaten reindeer calf. Puncture marks in the neck showed that the golden eagle was not the culprit but the European lynx. Why, though, had it buried the carcass? Lynx do not usually do that. The scientists were puzzled, so again they watched and waited. Sure enough, the lynx made the attack and ate its fill, but then along

The Eurasian lynx is the largest of the lynx. It has a coat with dark spots in the summer and no markings in winter. The large, furry paws help the cat move swiftly over soft snow. It kills with a suffocating bite to the neck of its victim.

came a wolverine, which broke up the carcass with its powerful jaws and teeth and dragged it away piecemeal to be buried and cached for future consumption. The mystery was solved, and the golden eagle exonerated, but to this day such myths and legends still persist.

LEGENDARY KILLERS

WOLVES HAVE HAD a bad press, but there is little evidence to suggest that wolves deliberately attack people. Despite this, the wolf takes the villain's role in fairy tales and other stories from around the world. It is the symbol of evil and a frequent predator of man, or so the stories go. Curiously, many of the 'true stories' are identical, no matter where they come from. Inevitably, it is a cold winter's night and the hero is alone or with his trusty dog. The wolves howl while they are hunting human prey, bare their teeth when attacking and have super strength. In reality, wolves hunt silently, only bare their teeth at other wolves, and are about as strong as a German shepherd dog. Indeed, there are few credible cases of wolves attacking people; after all, men are feared by wolves, not hunted by them. Dogs, as incidents in the press during the past few years illustrate, are far more dangerous, for they are familiar with and not afraid of people.

Sharks have received the same treatment. There is no doubt that sharks attack people, but there is growing evidence that many attacks are either a case

The golden eagle hunts by flying low and searching for prey methodically, criss-crossing a patch of ground. Small mammals, such as hares, birds, such as willow grouse, reptiles and sometimes fish, such as salmon, are taken in the talons in a brief and sudden rush. The habit of feeding at the carcasses of domestic stock, such as sheep or reindeer, has given the bird an undeserved reputation as a regular livestock killer.

of mistaken identity, for example, surfers resembling seals and sea-lions, or the result of aggressive territorial behaviour on the part of the shark. Other cases include people putting themselves at risk - spear fishermen carrying dead fish that dangle from their belt or bathers swimming into areas where sharks are known to hunt. Actual attacks, where the shark is to blame, are few. More people are killed each year by lightning than are attacked and killed by sharks, yet every summer the headlines are the same.

Large eagles are viewed with suspicion and feature in many wildlife tales. Nearly always the story is a child snatched up and taken away to the eagle's nest, but in this case, some of these stories are true.

In 1977, a 10-year-old child from Illinois was lifted off the ground by a large bird of prey and carried 30ft or so. In 1978, in the Middle East, there were three cases of eagles taking babies from river-banks while their mothers were washing clothes. And in 1932, there is the well-documented incident of a 4-year-old Norwegian girl who was snatched from a farmyard and carried off by a golden eagle. The eagle could barely lift her, but managed to carry her to the

head of a valley, where it dropped her on to a ledge. Local people saw the eagle circling overhead and were able to rescue her.

But, perhaps, the most extraordinary tale is of Jeanne Cowden of South Africa, who hand-fed a black eagle that lived in the Golden Gate Highlands. Miss Cowden felt very uncomfortable if the bird swooped when she was close to the cliff edge, and thought that given half a chance it might push her off. Black eagles have a reputation for pushing prey off ledges in order to dispatch it quickly before eating.

Miss Cowden decided to mount an experiment. She made a full-size effigy of herself, dressed it in her usual mountain-walking clothes and sat it at the cliff top. Sure enough, the eagle swooped in, grabbed the dummy, dragged it to the edge and pulled it over. The dummy fell hundreds of feet into the valley, and Miss Cowden's fear was vindicated.

CURIOUS TALES, BUT TRUE

A BLACK BEAR in Idaho made a habit of eating the udders of nursing ewes. Occasionally it would take the heart and liver but left the rest of the animal.

In harsh winters, when food is very scarce, the New Zealand kea climbs on to the backs of sheep, tears away the wool and eats the flesh underneath.

Red deer on a Scottish island chew on the nest-bound chicks of terns and gulls. Deer are normally herbivores, but their island diet lacks calcium and other salts and minerals. The deer obtain their calcium from the bones of the baby birds.

In northern Ohio, North American badgers have been accused of breaking into graves in a graveyard. They normally dig rapidly into the burrows of ground squirrels and moles, killing and eating the inhabitants.

The raccoon washes its food, usually crayfish or frogs, before it eats. Why it does this is unknown.

Stone martens in Germany and Switzerland have taken to biting the electrical parts on automobiles. In a single night, one Munich-based marten disabled 100 cars in a car park, and one German car manufacturer found that 10,000 of its cars were damaged in this way each year. The problem is that young martens test what is food and what is inedible by biting. The engine compartment of a car is a comfortable refuge and so the electrical connections there are checked out first by a marten family. In the autumn, by which time they have discovered that cars do not make good eating, the car damage drops off. Nevertheless, a summer's trying and testing had Swiss drivers making 3,000 insurance claims for stone marten damage.

The hagfish, an eel-shaped, deep-sea relative of the lamprey, ties itself in knots. With a circular mouth filled with sharp teeth, it fastens itself firmly to a victim, usually a large fish. Then, it forms a knot at the tail end, which it slowly slides up its slimy body towards its head. The knot is then used as a lever which helps the hagfish bore into its prey. Once inside, it eats the victim from the inside out.

Leatherback turtles, growing to 8ft long, are the world's largest sea turtles, yet they feast on nothing more substantial than jellyfish.

The lammergeier takes large bones in its talons and flies high above a rocky outcrop. It then drops the bones in order to smash them, extract the marrow, and waffle down beak-size splinters of bone. It does the same with tortoises.

Butcher birds or shrikes impale their prey on thorns or barbed wire, making

The great grey shrike is aptly nicknamed 'the butcher bird'. Small birds in flight and mouse-like rodents are caught and brought back to a favourite perch, where they are impaled on thorns or sharp twigs. The bird returns to its 'larder' periodically to feed. This shrike has 'spiked' an injured sparrow, but it might tackle birds the size of blackbirds and other thrushes.

it both easier to eat and to store. The macabre larder of a butcher bird may contain the impaled corpses of many animals, including small birds, mammals and insects.

REGIMENTED RANKS OF ANTS

TALES OF ARMY ANTS in South America and driver ants in Africa are legendary, but many of the tales are true. Army ants are formidable predators, but only if the entire army works together. Great columns of these ants are capable of killing every living thing in their path and a colony on the move might contain over half-a-million individuals.

A tethered horse or cow, or even an injured person unable to get up, can be stripped to the bone in a few hours. In one report from central Brazil, a column of ants 1 mile long and $^1/_2$ mile wide was seen advancing on the town. The police chief and few of the townsfolk tried to stop the ants and were killed for their troubles. The advance was only checked by men with flame-throwers.

The secret of the army ant's success is the ability of the entire colony to work as one, a gigantic super-organism. Communicating with other members of the colony by smell and vibrations, each individual has its role to play, whether it be foraging, defending the colony, or attending the egg-laying queen.

Food mostly consists of hard-bodied creatures - such as other insects, spiders and scorpions, and the colony is constantly on the move to find new supplies. Movements are not constant; instead, a 15-day nomadic phase alternates with a 20-day sedentary phase. After a couple of weeks travelling through the forest, the colony comes to a halt and sets up a semi-permanent camp. It stays there for about 20 days while the queen lays her latest batch of 50,000-100,000 eggs. The workers, in the meantime, go out and scour the forest for food. They forage in

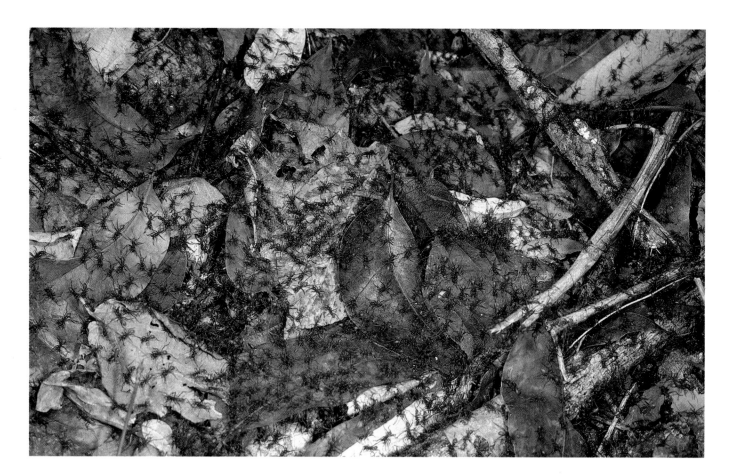

a fixed pattern, radiating from the camp like the spokes of a wheel. On day one, the columns head off in one direction, and the next day they take a compass heading exactly 123 degrees in another direction. By varying their direction in this way, they ensure that they do not comb the same piece of forest twice.

When the eggs hatch and a new army of mouths must be fed, the colony returns once more to a nomadic lifestyle. At dawn, columns of workers, guarded at intervals by large-jawed soldiers, set out from the daily bivouac and go hunting. Maintaining a constant compass heading, they travel at about 15yds per hour over a distance of 200yds per day, during which they gather 30,000 food items. Anything that cannot escape is caught.

Scuttling to and from the bivouac, where the queen and her entourage spend the day, there can be over 200,000 ants in a column. Side streams split off from the main column and spread out to form a raiding front up to 20yds wide. Streams are not a barrier. Workers simply interlock legs and form a living bridge over which the colony can pass. If caught in a flood, the colony rolls into a large ball and floats to safety.

In the evening, the queen's bivouac unravels like a ball of wool and follows the route of the day's raiding column. They travel under the cover of darkness for about 8 hours to the next bivouac site, about 90yds along the trail, setting up temporary camp before dawn breaks.

In some parts of the world army and driver ants are not feared, but welcomed. If a column of ants is heading for their home, local village folk will just leave until the ants have passed through. The ants strip the houses of vermin, snakes, scorpions and insects. The inhabitants return to a house which is pest-free.

A raiding party of army ants scours the forest for victims. Every living thing unable to escape the onslaught is killed, dismembered and taken back to camp. The army is like one single, gigantic 'super-organism', each individual playing its role for the good of the whole group.

Army ants do not restrict their wanderings to the forest floor. They forage in the canopy for the nests of tree termites, other species of ants, wasps and bees. These army ants are removing the larvae from a tropical wasp nest.

One advantage of working as a well-disciplined army is that army ants can overpower prey, such as this katydid (New World grasshopper), that is much bigger than themselves.

◄

At the centre of an army ant daytime bivouac is the queen. She is tended and fed by workers and her only task is to produce eggs - millions of them. At dusk, the bivouac disbands and the queen and her entourage move to a new site. A nomadic lifestyle prevents the colony from running out of food.

▼

A stream is no barrier to army ants. They simply join legs and build a bridge of living bodies over which the rest of the colony can pass.

Raccoons mostly forage alone at night, usually near streams in which they 'wash' their food. It is not clear whether the raccoon is simply manipulating its food or actually cleaning it of dirt or noxious substances. Prey includes fish, crayfish, frogs, birds and eggs.

In Lapland, the golden eagle
has been accused of taking
baby reindeer calves. No doubt
it scavenges on the carcasses of
still-born calves and is capable
of grabbing a new-born one.
But by far the most calves are
killed by lynx and the leftovers
are buried by wolverines or
'gluttons'.

► Anacondas can grow to over 20ft (6.1m) in length and can tackle large prey, which they kill by constriction. This anaconda has taken on an equally powerful cayman ... and won.

The egg-eating snake, as its name suggests, eats eggs, but the remarkable thing is that it swallows them whole. The jaws dislocate and the egg is manoeuvred into the throat. Projections from the spinal cord break the egg shell when it is inside.

Pirates, Scroungers & Hangers-on

9

Why should a hunter expend enormous amounts of energy in catching food, when it can save all that time and effort, and reduce the uncertainty of gaining a meal, by scrounging food or stealing it from another predator?

Piracy or kleptoparasitism involves the procurement of food by one individual, such as an Arctic tern, only to be stolen by another, like a herring gull. The pirate may take the food from the grasp of the predator, worry it until the food is dropped, or force it to regurgitate food that it has already swallowed. Pirates tend to be persistent and violent, harassing successful predators for long periods of time until they give up their prey. Scavenging is common in the animal world. Even the top predators, like lions and hyenas, are not averse to taking over an already dead body, and often they will steal prey from each other. Compulsive scavengers, like large vultures, rarely kill for themselves; instead, they wait for the prey to die or be killed for them by other predators. Maribou storks take scavenging a stage further and do not wait for their 'corpses' to die. They patrol the edges of grassland fires, risking a singeing, and pick off creatures injured by the flames or disorientated by the smoke.

Some small predators also specialise in the misfortune of others. Insects which have ditched in a pond and are trapped by the surface film are attacked from above by pondskaters and from below by waterboatmen and trout. And the larvae of petroleum flies live in the most unlikely habitat imaginable - in slicks of crude oil. They grab any trapped insects with their mouthhooks and bore through the skin in order to get at the soft parts inside.

Bird Pirates

Skuas, gulls and frigate birds are the pirates of the bird world. Arctic skuas dive-bomb puffins and other seabirds in an attempt to steal their catch. The puffin may have flown a long way with its catch, but the skua grabs it by the wingtip and tilts it into the sea. The puffin's only recourse is to jettison its food and then the skua will let go. Displaying considerable aerobatic skill, the skua catches the falling package in mid-air.

Seabirds, particularly gulls, skuas and frigate birds, tend to be the pirates of the bird world. These grey-headed gulls at Lake St Lucia in Natal are mobbing an egret in order to steal the fish it has caught.

Light-Fingered Hunters

Not all pirates irritate their host. There are smaller, less obvious pirates. On the webs of large, orb-web spiders there are sometimes tiny, sneak-thief spiders which creep across the web and steal pieces of food without alerting the host. Other scroungers do not steal a meal but scrounge a ride. Nature's hitchhikers include fish and birds which rely on other, usually larger and more powerful, hunters to take them where they want to go. On land, small, agile animals rely on larger, clumsy ones to flush prey from the undergrowth.

Some gulls shadow diving birds, such as ducks and cormorants, and attack them as soon as they reach the surface. Gulls have been seen to perch right on the large beaks of pelicans trying to get them to release the fish they have just caught. Gulls also harass terns, chasing them mercilessly until they drop their hard-won catch. Black-headed gulls accompany lapwings foraging for earth-worms in fields. The lapwings find and pull the worms from the soil, only to be chased away by the gulls who steal their food. The gulls spread out amongst the lapwing flock, each gull watching the activities of several lapwings. During the course of a day, a gull can steal more than 160 worms from its lapwing 'servants', which represent more than twice its daily nutritional requirements - clearly, a far less energetic and more reliable way of obtaining food than following the plough.

The most skilled flying pirates are the frigate birds. They swoop low over the water, dipping the head and beak into the waves and plucking small fish or squid quite literally from the jaws of pursuing tuna. This behaviour requires many years of practice and so younger birds take to intercepting other seabirds, pulling at tail feathers and dangling feet, forcing them to disgorge their catch. The frigate bird is able to outfly most other birds with some modifications of its flight system. It has the largest wingspan to body-weight ratio of any bird and it has a smaller quantity of oil in its feathers, reducing actual body weight. The lack of oil means that it cannot enter the water to catch its prey and must, therefore, depend, to a certain extent, on 'professional' piracy in order to obtain its food.

In India, black drongos sometimes chase smaller insect-eating birds, buzzing them until they drop their food. And in the New World, turkey vultures have discovered an easy way to get food from young, great blue herons. The very young chicks fall prey to the vultures, but the older birds defend themselves by regurgitating food and spitting it at their assailant. What better way for a vulture to obtain a partially digested meal that it can take straight back to its own chicks?

Aerial piracy seems to be commonest amongst birds that have a fairly catholic diet, and there are some surprises. Even little sparrows can be pirates. They have been seen to steal crickets and grasshoppers from digger wasps.

OLD WORLD VULTURES

OLD WORLD VULTURES, living in southern Europe, Africa and Asia, cannot smell dead bodies, as was once suggested. They spot food from long distances, and they are quick to take advantage. Many bloody battlefields were visited by vultures and badly injured soldiers, unable to move or fight back, were in danger of being attacked and torn apart by the birds. Ancient Abyssinian armies were said to be accompanied overhead by flocks of vultures, and shooting parties were dispatched to scare off the vulture flocks during the Crimean war. And the Parsee sect of India leave their dead at Towers of Silence, where vultures deal with the dead bodies, a throwback to times and places where the soil is not deep enough to bury the dead and there is insufficient wood for cremation.

Under more normal circumstances, vultures are highly developed as 'professional' scavengers. They are relatives of the birds of prey but rarely hunt. They often soar high above the East African plains, using thermals to gain height effortlessly. They have reasonable eyesight, not much better than our own, but they are good at watching for the tell-tale signs of food - maybe a carcass on the ground, predators actively hunting, and other vultures dropping down to feed. An 'eye-spy' chain of vultures watching other vultures can have birds homing in on a carcass from several miles away. Lions and leopards often haul their kills into the shelter of bushes to prevent the inevitable invasion.

East African carcasses have several species of vultures in attendance, each type specialised to exploit different parts of the body and, therefore, not in competition. Griffon vultures have a sharp-edged bill for cutting meat and a serrated tongue to help swallow it quickly. The crop can take a quarter of the bird's body weight in food. Griffons feed on the soft, fleshy parts, while others, like the aggressive, lappet-faced vultures, go for the skin, tendons and other coarse tissue. Egyptian vultures with their thin beaks pick up the leftovers. The head and neck of some species, like lappet-faced vultures, are naked, an adaptation that enables the birds to insert the head deep into a gory carcass without caking the plumage with blood.

And if they cannot find a carcass, vultures take to eating dung; but not just any old dung, they prefer that from big cats, ignoring dung from dogs and hyenas. Big cats, such as lions, do not digest their food as well as dogs do, and so lion dung has about 10 per cent more undigested food available for vultures. These birds, like the dogs, also have a highly efficient digestive system able to extract the last ounce of nutrients from what seems at first sight to be an unlikely source of food.

THE BARE BONES

VULTURES SOMETIMES DEPEND on other scavengers for survival. Vulture chicks need small slithers of bones from carcasses to provide them with calcium to build their own healthy bones. The meat regurgitated by their parents has little calcium so they must get their supplies from these bone fragments. The vultures themselves have not learned, like the lammergeier, how to break the bones and so they rely on creatures like spotted hyenas, with their powerful teeth and

Vultures spot other vultures dropping down to a carcass and, like a bush telegraph, vultures from a large area will gather to feed. These lappet-faced and white-backed vultures must compete with a golden jackal for a carcass.

jaws, to break up skeletons. The hyenas tend to ignore the very small fragments, but they are essential to the vulture chicks.

In South Africa, however, it was noticed that the chicks of Cape vultures in nests adjoining ranch lands were deformed. Hyenas are excluded from these areas and so any dead carcasses, particularly the skeletons, remain intact and the vulture chicks fail to obtain the necessary calcium. By the time a skeleton breaks down by decay, the calcium is leached out, so the only solution was for local conservationists to put out small piles of crushed and broken bones for the vultures to take.

NEW WORLD VULTURES

SOME NEW WORLD VULTURES do locate food by smell and have well-developed nostrils. Although labelled with the same 'vulture' name, they are more closely related to storks than birds of prey, but they have filled the same ecological niche - an example of convergent evolution (two unrelated animals solving the same ecological problem in the same way). The ability to smell carrion offers New World vultures the opportunity to find food in the dense forests of South America. Fresh corpses tend to go unnoticed for they have no strong smell, but a carcass a day old or more can be located. Rotting carcasses are ignored for vultures prefer reasonably fresh meat.

The scavengers gather to clear-up the leftovers at a wildebeest carcass. At the Etosha Pan, food can be scarce at certain times of the year and so competition is fierce. Black-backed jackals appear to have the upper hand as they chase away the vultures.

The vultures with the best olfactory sense are the ubiquitous turkey vulture and the yellow-headed vulture. They arrive first, to be followed by black and king vultures, which will displace their predecessors from the food site. The large king vulture, with its powerful bill, is able to tear at skin and tendons, while the smaller species take the softer tissues.

The largest of the New World vultures is the Andean condor, an inhabitant of mountains and valleys. These enormous birds with wingspans reaching 10$\frac{1}{2}$ft (3.2m) across, scour the hillsides for carrion. In certain parts of the Andes, they fly to the coast, exploiting a food bonanza of afterbirth tissues during the seal and sea-lion breeding seasons.

MEAT-EATING BEES

ON THANKSGIVING DAY recently, a US scientist was working in Panama and he put out the carcass of the traditional Thanksgiving turkey for the local cats to enjoy. Imagine then his surprise when the first of the scavengers to arrive was a swarm of bees. They were stingless bees that had previously been seen over dead bodies, but it was thought they were only after the body juices. When the scientist examined them more closely, however, he found that they have 5 large, pointed teeth on each mandible, a rather unusual arrangement for bees to have, and he discovered that they use these to cut through flesh.

Scout bees head out from the colony and search, not for flowers, but for carrion. Dead frogs or lizards are preferred. If they find a suitable corpse, they lay down a pheromone (smell) trail and recruit more help. The bees then descend on the body in large numbers. Any competition, such as flies, is frightened away and the bees take over. First they settle on the outside of the carcass and form a circle. Using the specially adapted mandibles, they begin to tear at the skin, making a hole through which the rest of the swarm can enter and eat away the insides. As they chew, they spread an enzyme over the meat. This partially digests the food so that it can be carried back to the nest, where it is regurgitated to others. A frog is reduced to its bare bones by 60-80 bees in about 3 hours, but a 1,000-strong swarm may tackle a dead monkey or ant-eater and strip it down in a few days.

Aiding and abetting them might be a species of ant. The ants appear to be tolerated by the bees, some kind of chemical interaction between the ants and the bees preventing the latter from ousting the former from the site. The mutual tolerance is aided by the fact that the two species work a shift system: bees by day and ants by night.

ARMY FOLLOWERS

ARMY ANTS, LIKE most armies, have their followers. An advancing column of raiders is accompanied by an entire menagerie of animals, each one intent on taking advantage of the panic and mayhem created by the ants. Antbirds are the most obvious. They do not eat the ants themselves but prey upon the insects that are flushed out ahead of the ant columns.

There are many species of antbirds, and each one has its place in the pecking order. The most dominant birds station themselves just ahead of the ant columns, where the most insects are flushed out, lesser mortals taking positions beside and behind the army. In the trees above a whole procession of birds follow, not relying on the ants but on the special 'sentinel' services of the antbirds. Antbirds tend to be alert for predators, and are often the first birds to spot a hunting hawk that might swoop through the understorey and grab a small bird. The other birds depend on the antbirds' alarm calls.

One bird has discovered that it can take advantage of its privileged position and cheat its competitors in the race for the choicest morsels. If a grasshopper jumps from the grass and a rival bird is about to snatch it, the antbird gives its alarm call. The other bird is startled and would rather lose an insect than its life, and so it takes evading action. The cheat, meanwhile, scoops up the prey.

HITCH A RIDE ON A BUFFALO

ON AFRICAN SAVANNAH, cattle egrets follow rhinos, elephants and buffalo, relying on these large mammals to flush insects from the grass. The birds perch on the backs of their unknowing accomplices and dart down to pick off a cricket or grasshopper that is disturbed. Birds associated with large, herbivorous mammals use a third less energy by hitching a ride and collect 50 per cent more insects than those birds hunting alone. Cattle egrets have become so successful that they have spread east and west, colonising much of South America in the wake of expanding cattle herds.

Cattle egrets do not feed on the external parasites, such as ticks and flies, that live on the mammals. These are gobbled up by the tick-birds or ox-peckers. Ox-peckers probe into every crease, crevice and orifice in search of parasites, and they are often seen with their slightly vertically flattened beak pecking at the corners of eyes, and in the ears and nostrils, levering off ticks. They have similar features and behave rather like woodpeckers, with sharp claws to gain a hold on rhino and buffalo hides and stiffened tail feathers to help them move over the vertical surfaces.

Bee-eaters have also found that an association with a larger creature can increase the chances of hunting success. They forsake the large mammals, preferring to ride on the backs of African bustards and ostriches. As the larger bird moves through the grass, their small passengers dart out to catch the insects that are disturbed.

Yellow-billed hornbills follow parties of dwarf mongooses and snatch small creatures that the mongooses miss. The mongooses tolerate the birds for they warn them of any danger.

The most extraordinary association, however, is that of the Egyptian plover (and other plovers) and the Nile crocodile. The plovers not only take parasites from the crocodile's hide, but they are also reputed to enter the open mouths of resting crocodiles and pick particles of food from their teeth.

BARBERS AND DENTISTS

CLEANER WRASSE WERE originally small fish that fed on the tiny, parasitic crustaceans clinging to the skin of other fishes. They became so adept at parasite removal that fish began to queue up to be disinfested. Thus, the cleaner wrasse became a specialist and today small fish, such as gobies, and large fish, like groupers, come to specific 'cleaning stations' where several wrasse give them a good clean. Even giant manta rays rely on their services. Some fish come from a mile or so away.

The blue-and-white wrasse first perform a little dance, indicating that they are open for business. The customer hangs motionless in the water, as the wrasse groom the skin and the inside of the mouth and gills, including the teeth. The grouper could swallow the smaller cleaners in one gulp, but it does not. Instead, it stops all predatory activity until the cleaning is over.

The wrasse, it seems, are very important for a healthy, coral-reef community. If the fish are removed experimentally, the customers either move away or suffer considerably from ulcers, frayed fins and fungal diseases.

There are also cleaner shrimps that wave their antennae to attract customers. They clamber about, removing fungi, parasites and food particles from the skin, mouth and gills. As one marine biologist was quick to point out: 'Fishes have thousands of scales for "things" to get under and create annoyance, but no fingers with which to scratch.' Cleaner wrasse and shrimps provide that service for them.

One small fish, however, mimics the cleaner wrasse and, having fooled the

African buffalo disturb insects in the grass, which are snatched by the accompanying band of white cattle egrets. On the buffalo itself, ticks and other external parasites provide food for the oxpeckers that scramble about on its hide.

The remora is a hitchhiker in the sea. A dorsal fin modified as a 'sucker' enables the fish to obtain a free ride from slow-swimming sharks and giant rays.

customer, takes a bite out of its tail. The false cleaner is one of the blenny family. It has the shape and blue-and-white pattern of the wrasse and looks remarkably like it. When the customers line up, the blenny is allowed to approach as close as it pleases, but instead of a quiet nibble at the parasites, the blenny uses its underslung mouth with long teeth to take a chunk out of the flesh, the fin edges or scales. The customer, thus duped, is very wary of visiting that cleaning station again.

HITCHHIKERS

REMORAS ARE SPECIALLY adapted to ride on the undersides and topside of large, slow-swimming sharks, manta rays and sea turtles. The dorsal fin is modified into a sucker on the top of the head with which they can cling on tight and ride the oceans for free. The flat fin rays, resembling the ridged sole of a shoe inside the sucker, can be manipulated in such a way to create a vacuum between the remora and its travelling companion and so the hitchhiker can stick fast no matter how quickly the host is travelling.

What the remoras get from this association is not clear. They get the free ride, and it is thought they take advantage of the scraps of food that inevitably fall from the table of the shark. Some have been seen in mouths and gill chambers behaving like cleaner fish. Certainly, the stomach contents of remoras include a high proportion of parasitic copepods and isopods. In the Yucatan caves, where large sharks go to bathe in fresh-water currents, remoras have been seen to eat the parasites that have been dislodged. In the Bimini lagoon, remoras dart in to eat the afterbirth debris following lemon shark births.

They are not totally at sea when detached from their host and have been observed feeding alone. A group of remoras swims in circles with the largest fish stacked on top of the smallest ones.

In addition to the remora, there are several types of sucker fish, including the sharksucker (which rides the shark's bow wave), the white suckerfish and the whale sucker, which, as its name implies, attaches itself to large, baleen whales.

Remoras have appeared in ancient tales. They were thought to slow down ships; indeed, the Greeks called it the 'ship-holder'. Emperor Caligula was delayed on his voyage to Antium by remoras, as was Mark Antony's ship at Actium. Mark Antony lost a battle and Caligula lost his life. Remoras have also been ground up and used in potions to 'delay' childbirth and extend love-making. In Madagascar, dried remora was placed around the neck of an unfaithful spouse in order that he or she would return to the partner and 'stick'. And there were stories told by Christopher Columbus of natives in the Caribbean tethering remoras on lines and getting them to attach to sea turtles that could then be hauled in.

Some hangers-on, like black-and-white, zebra-striped pilot fish, do not actually ride, but are ready to grab a titbit from their outsize partners, usually a shark, ray or giant grouper. At one time, it was thought that they guided the larger swimming companion, but it is more likely that they are seeking a safe refuge; and what better place than near the business end of a shark? Pilot fish are careful not to get too close to the jaws, but copy every move the larger fish makes, perhaps trying to ride on the pressure wave ahead of its snout.

Cleaner fish and shrimps divest sharks of their parasites, lemon sharks and nurse sharks resting on the bottom. Nurse sharks will even stop all gill movements for up to 2 minutes while they have their gill chambers cleaned.

Marabou storks are opportunists. When other birds begin to breed, marabou storks take to feeding on their chicks. In dense flamingo colonies there is a surfeit of young bodies and the storks are quick to seize an unguarded chick. All animals are vulnerable at waterholes and marabou storks are ready to take advantage of their nervousness. In Etosha, they hunt doves. And if live food is unavailable, marabous join vultures and scavenge at a bloody wildebeest carcass.

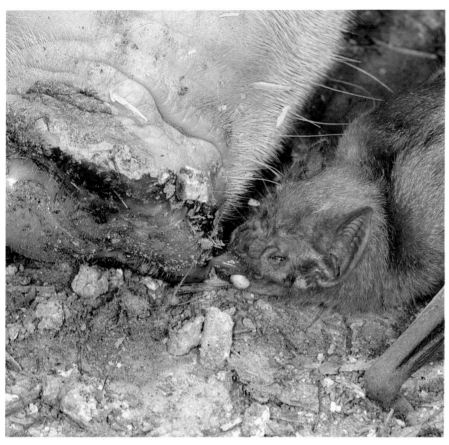

The oxpecker not only picks off external parasites, but also pecks at sores and keeps them open in order to get at the blood. This has been taken to an extreme by the sharp-billed finch of the Galapagos, which has come to depend on blood from larger birds, such as masked boobies, for food. It is also known as the 'vampire finch'. The true 'vampires' are small bats from South and Central America. They have very sharp teeth with which they take a slice of skin out from their victim, often domestic stock like pigs, and then lick the blood.

Skuas are real pirates. They attack and rob numerous other birds, by preying directly on small species and the chicks of larger ones, or by bothering them to such an extent they disgorge food which has already been caught. A bonxie or great skua attacks a gannet (below), while Antarctic skuas take a gentoo penguin chick (right), harass adelie penguin chicks (far right), and break into a giant petrel egg (below right).

On the Defence

10

The relationship between predators and prey is constantly changing. Sometimes predators have the upper hand, but sometimes the hunted outwit the hunters.

The first line of defence must be alertness. Potential prey must have well-developed senses capable of picking up the first signs of an approaching predator. An audible alarm helps others to respond, and in the ensuing scramble a predator might be disorientated. Given the warning, the next strategy is to escape ... rapidly. Speed is a defence used by many animals and some actually demonstrate their fitness to the predator in a display that says 'You can't catch me.' Other animals have displays which say 'Try and catch me' and, in so doing, distract the predator away from nests or youngsters. Plovers pretend to have broken wings and flap about very convincingly until they deem it safe to take off and fly normally. Taken to its extreme, some animals feign death. Many hunters are motivated by movement and so by lying motionless an animal reduces a predator's interest and may avoid its attention altogether. This behaviour in opossums gave rise to the expression 'playing possum'.

ALARM CALLS

MANY SPECIES OF potential prey animals have developed warning codes which increase their chances of survival. Robins give a thin, high-pitched call when a hawk is flying overhead. Other garden birds have similar, non-locatable, wispy calls that give the alarm without giving away their position. Only one bird might spot the predator, but all the birds in the neighbourhood are on the alert, no matter the species.

Belding's ground squirrels, living in North America, give calls that distinguish between predators, such as badgers, that can enter their tunnels and those, like coyotes, that cannot.

In East Africa, vervet monkeys have specific alarm calls for specific predators. Researchers have identified a leopard alarm for spotted cats, a snake alarm for pythons and a hawk alarm for birds of prey. Each alarm triggers a particular escape behaviour. In response to the leopard alarm, the troop climbs into the uppermost branches of the trees, where a leopard would be too heavy to go. The snake alarm has all the monkeys standing on their hind legs, looking for the location of the snake. And the hawk alarm has them scattering for the bushes. An eagle could pluck a monkey from the branches, so hiding in the trees would be inappropriate and possibly fatal.

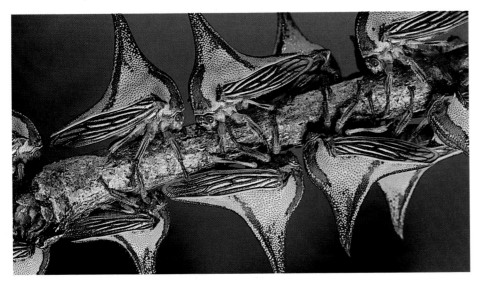

Looking to all the world like spines on a plant, these thorn bugs are protected both by the sharp, thorn-like projection on the back and by camouflage as they feed on the sap.

PUZZLING BEHAVIOUR

Confusion is a valuable defensive weapon. If prey can do something unpredictable or startling, a hunter may be left wondering what to do next. Predators can also be fooled by appearances. The menacing 'eyespots' on a butterfly's wings may seem threatening to predators. Stripes and bright colours say 'Keep off, I'm poisonous' - some are genuine, but others are bogus. By adopting the defensive coloration of a known poisonous look-alike, a non-poisonous creature can gain a measure of immunity to attack. Defensive coloration is most effective when it enables an animal to disappear, and camouflage is an effective way of avoiding being caught.

If danger threatens, springbok leap vertically into the air and bounce around with stiff legs, a behaviour known as 'pronking'. It is thought that the antelope is demonstrating to the predator that it is too fit to catch.

FAST GETAWAY

WHEN THERE IS nowhere to hide, there is only one solution - run. The pronghorn of the open prairies of western North America must outrun wolves and coyotes and to do so have developed, not only speed that is only rivalled by the cheetah, but also stamina. Pronghorns, which resemble antelopes but are classified in a subfamily of their own, can run hard and long. Their top speed is about 55mph (82km/h), achieved with 27ft (8.2m) strides of their slender legs, and 45mph (72km/h) can be maintained for mile after tortuous mile. It is achieved by modifications of the body.

Pronghorns have unusually large lungs and heart, which pumps more oxygenated blood to the muscles of the legs. They also have more of the cell organelles, known as mitochondria, in each muscle cell. These convert the additional oxygen into energy. Five times as much oxygen is available to a pronghorn than, say, a mountain goat.

Antelopes and gazelles use alertness and speed to flee a predator, but they also have another curious piece of behaviour, known as pronking, which might intimidate or confuse a predator. They jump vertically into the air and appear to bounce along stiff legs, all four legs hitting the ground at the same time. The springbok of southern Africa is the champion pronker. As it leaps, the fan or crest of white hairs on the back are erected, and the head is bent forward and down almost to the feet. The hooves are kept together and the back is arched. At the moment it touches the ground, it springs back up again, sometimes jumping straight up, other times leaping forwards or jigging sharply to one side. Then, it lowers its fan, raises its head and races away at full speed.

Pronking is infectious. First one or two animals will start, and soon the rest of the herd will join in. The jumps are thought to indicate to the predator the

animal's fitness and its ability to escape. The message is twofold. Firstly, it is telling the hunter that it has been spotted, and secondly, it is encouraging the predator to chase after other prey which it is more likely to catch. The springbok is demonstrating that it is in full control of the situation and that the predator would be wasting time and energy in chasing it.

This hawk-moth caterpillar attempts to frighten off an aggressor by mimicking a snake, even to the extent of having large eyespots.

CONFUSE THE ENEMY

TROPICAL TIGER MOTHS 'jam' the sonar system of pursuing bats. The moth emits a burst of sound which startles the bat, just as it is about to attack. Other moths, tuning into the frequencies which bats use for echolocation, take evasive action at the moment of attack. Yet others foil pursuit by simply folding their wings and dropping out of the sky.

Flying fish flee the opposite way. Pursued by tuna or other fast-swimming fish, flying fish leap clear of the water and glide in the air. There are 'two-wingers' with enlarged pectoral fins, and 'four-wingers' possessing wing-like pectoral and pelvic fins. The total 'wing' area is the same, but four-wingers fly slightly further and in rougher sea conditions than two-wingers.

In order to leave the water, the flying fish accelerates towards the surface, breaking through at an angle of about 30 degrees. The wings are expanded and, maintaining the same angle, the tail remains in the water and waggles at 50-70 strokes per second, propelling the fish along the surface. This is the 'taxiing' stage, which is followed by take-off. At an air-speed of 49-66ft (15-20m) per second, a flight of 55yds (50m) can be achieved at a height of 25ft (8m) above the sea's surface. At this point the fish drops back to the surface, gives another waggle of its tail, and takes off again without submerging. It can travel for about 437yds (400m) in half a minute.

Lizard fish bury into the sand on the seabed to escape predators, and creatures living in deserts, such as lizards, beetles and snakes, adopt the same strategy.

Squid, cuttlefish and octopuses confuse predators using a cloud of ink. The cloud is usually the same size and shape as the escapee, and serves as dummy prey on which the predator can try to bite. Meanwhile, the cunning cephalopod has changed colour and shot off in another direction, using its water-powered siphon as a means of jet-propulsion.

Confusion can be further enhanced by offering a predator something expendable. Many lizards are able to discard their tail, leaving the hunter a small meal but allowing the prey a chance to flee and grow another tail.

Some butterflies, such as the grayling, have small eyespots on the edges of

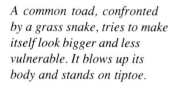

A common toad, confronted by a grass snake, tries to make itself look bigger and less vulnerable. It blows up its body and stands on tiptoe.

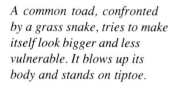

A caterpillar from the tropical rainforest of Mexico is protected by spiky hairs. Its bright colours warn predators that if they tried to attack they would receive an unpleasant mouthful.

their wings. This is an attempt to misdirect the pecks of predatory birds away from the vulnerable body and focus instead on the less vital wing edge. And judging by the number of butterflies to be seen with triangular chunks taken out of the wing, leaving the body intact and in working order, it is successful.

Other butterflies have false heads, the head being the most vulnerable part of the body and the obvious target for a predator. Some have the head on the wing tips, well away from the real head. Its appearance is enhanced by antennae-like projections and eyespots. One tropical hair-streak even has brown-and-white stripes that direct a predator's attention directly towards the false head. It even behaves in a way to confuse an attacker. On landing, it turns around and is, therefore, ready to flee in the opposite direction to which the predator expects it to fly.

FALSE EYES AND FRIGHTENING COLOURS

FOR THE SLOW animals or the ones that have been cornered, all is not lost. They have a few tricks up their sleeve ... or under their wings, on their belly or on their back, to intimidate the enemy. Some praying mantids open their wings and flash gaudy-coloured undersurfaces. The display is strengthened when the insect produces a hissing sound, by rubbing its abdomen rapidly between its wings. One species has brightly coloured legs, which it holds up to scare off predators. One was observed to see off a monkey.

Some butterflies open their wings and startle a predator by presenting it with large eyespots. Hawk moths at rest have their wings in the familiar triangular position, but if threatened, they open their wings wide to expose two large eyespots. These are not on the edge of the wings, like smaller eyespots, but are close to the abdomen where the combination of body parts resembles the face of something far bigger and more frightening. Underwing moths have camouflaged forewings. The hunter is either surprised and the moth escapes, or it pecks at the edge of the coloured wing without damaging the moth's body.

The ultimate in caterpillars must be the way some of them mimic snakes. The sphinx caterpillar of Central America is the most skilled exponent. At rest it resembles a twig, but under threat its front end drops down from the branch and inflates into a triangular, snake's-head shape, complete with eyespots and movements that resemble a snake striking.

One of the South American toads has eyespots painted on its bottom. If danger threatens, it raises its rear legs, blows up its body and turns its back on its assailant. If the predator persists, the toad produces an unpleasant substance from glands close to the false eyes.

Sometimes the warning is genuine and the prey really does have something dangerous or obnoxious in reserve. One of the arctiid moths opens its wings to display red or yellow blotches on its abdomen, while, at the same time, exuding a foul-tasting substance.

The skunk's first line of defence is its conspicuous black-and-white fur pattern. It is a warning. If the colour code fails, the creature reinforces its warning. The large, striped skunk arches its back, stamps its feet, waves its head from side to side, and struts around with its tail and head in the air. If that fails

When resting, the eyed hawk moth matches the tree-trunk on which it sits, but if it is disturbed it opens its forewings and flashes large, false eyes on the hind wings.

The black-and-white pattern of the striped skunk alone warns an intruder not to come closer, but if it persists the skunk turns its back, raises its tail and squirts an evil-smelling substance that irritates the eyes and is difficult to remove.

to impress, it turns about and points it rear end at the aggressor, squirting a sticky, evil-smelling liquid from large anal glands. The spray can hit a predator 6ft (2m) away with considerable accuracy and can reach one at 30ft (10m) with a following wind. The spray itself contains proteins that latch on chemically to hair and are thus difficult to remove. A hunter that has received a faceful of 'skunk juice' is unlikely ever to forget it.

CHEMICAL DEFENCE

THE BEST FORM of defence is attack, and that is just what some animals do to survive. Certain grasshoppers exude repellent substances from the abdomen, and millipedes actually produce hydrogen cyanide from pores along their body. But the star defender in this miniature theatre of war is the bombadier beetle. If grabbed by a frog or toad, the beetle discharges its chemical weapon, leaving the unfortunate amphibian with a sore and throbbing tongue. If an ant should hold on to a leg, the beetle swivels its abdomen round and squirts a boiling blast of noxious chemicals directly at it. Under constant attack from a swarm of ants, the beetle is able to discharge the scalding fluid 20-30 times, and make good its escape.

The defensive spray is produced in a combustion chamber at the tip of the beetle's abdomen.Two chemicals are mixed with a cocktail of enzymes to produce an explosive propellant and a chemical irritant. The spray is released in pulses, like a machine-gun, at a rate of 500-1,000 pulses per second. By pulsing the jet, the beetle achieves greater spray impact, but more importantly it does not blow off its own behind. The pulsed nature of the reaction prevents overheating in the explosion chamber.

Another less-advanced relative of the bombadier beetle, one of the paussine beetles, delivers its spray in a different way. The gland openings are spaced out on each side of the body, near the tip of the abdomen, but instead of directing it at the predator, it employs a principle of physics, hitherto only known to have been used by man. The principle is the Coanda effect, and it is seen when milk has the annoying propensity to curl round the lip of the jug and on to the table-cloth. In the case of the paussine beetle, there is a flange on either side of the abdomen, next to the gland openings. When attacked from behind or the side, the abdomen can be directed at the attacker, but the beetle cannot point its abdomen to the front. So, if the insect is under frontal assault, the jet of boiling liquid can bend a full 50 degrees, following the curve of the body, and be directed forwards.

Yet another relative, a metrine beetle, does not squirt a jet at all, but simply allows the chemicals to boil out from under the flanges of its wing covers. During an attack, the beetle froths in a bubbling mass of boiling secretion, the bursting bubbles sending tiny droplets of chemicals in all directions. Surrounded by this defensive vapour, the beetle is able to walk nonchalantly through a whole swarm of would-be predators without coming to any harm.

WARNING COLOURS AND FALSE MIMICS

ARROW POISON FROGS, which exude the most deadly poisons known to man, are brightly coloured - a message to predators to leave well alone. Wasps rely on black-and-yellow stripes to warn of poisonous stings, and many brightly coloured caterpillars advertise their ability to cause irritation and pain if the hairs on their bodies are touched.

But the next best thing to having a chemical defence system is to **pretend** that you do. Harmless animals take on the appearance of poisonous ones and confer on themselves immunity from attack. The larvae of monarch butterflies in North America feed on milkweed plants and, in doing so, gain protective

The caterpillar of the monarch butterfly eats milkweeds from which it extracts a poison. The noxious chemical is retained during metamorphosis and so the butterfly is protected. It displays its unpalatability with gaudy colours. The viceroy caterpillar does not collect the poison, but the adult butterfly (below) mimics the warning colour of the monarch (left) and escapes being eaten by birds.

poisons that are separated and stored by the caterpillar. The caterpillar pupates and, after metamorphosis, the butterfly emerges complete with a chemical defence, for the milkweed poisons are retained.

The viceroy caterpillar looks completely different from that of the monarch and feeds on fairly innocuous plants. But when the viceroy butterfly emerges, it looks exactly like a monarch. The only difference is that it does not have the poisons. The viceroy mimics the monarch in order to confer immunity to attack; and it works. In tests, monarch butterflies have been presented to scrub jays. The birds might take one butterfly, but the reaction is so violent that they refuse to touch another monarch again. Presented with the harmless viceroys, the birds behave in the same way. They will not touch them.

HIDING AWAY

RABBITS RUN AWAY the moment danger threatens, scampering as fast as they can into their nearby burrows, but hares, out in the middle of the field, do not. Instead, they freeze, relying on their ability to blend in with the grass. The young of many other herbivores do the same. They only flee at the last moment, when they are certain they have been spotted.

Camouflage is a common means of defence, the simplest being counter-shading. Pelagic fish tend to be dark above and pale below. Seen from below, the white underside matches the light from the surface, and viewed from above the grey back blends in with the darkness of the deep. Grey-and-black stripes, like those on the mackerel, mimic the patterns made by scattered light as it passes through disturbed water.

In high latitudes or altitudes, animals adopt white fur or feathers in snow and mottled brown patterns when the snow has melted. Arctic animals, such as hares and ptarmigan, change their coats with the season. In the spring when the snow cover is patchy, the pattern is matched by the fur colour on their backs.

The willow grouse goes one better: it not only takes on the colours of its background but, in the face of danger, shuts down its entire body. Heartbeat is reduced to a mere tick-over and breathing rate drops dramatically. In the resting state, the willow grouse's heart pumps away at a comfortable 150 beats per minute, but if an Arctic fox approaches, the motionless bird reduces it to 20 beats per minute. Breathing rate drops by 70 per cent. This serves to reduce all signs of life to a minimum and suppresses the accidental release of any scent that might alert the predator. Dogs trained to seek out birds for research purposes have been seen to walk straight over a sitting bird. If, however, the predator discovers the grouse, a remarkable thing happens. In just 1 second, the heart rate suddenly accelerates from 20 beats to 600 and the bird explodes into the air.

BATTEN DOWN THE HATCHES

IF ALL ELSE FAILS, an animal can retreat completely from the world. Rabbits live in burrows and are careful to have an extra escape exit in case a polecat or weasel should call. Ground squirrels block their tunnel entrances at night to keep out unwelcome nocturnal predators.

Tortoises carry their defence on their back. Head and limbs can be pulled back into the shell, the tough carapace withstanding the attacks of many predators. Hermit crabs acquire their protective shell, taking over discarded whelk shells and the shells of other marine molluscs. Some even have sea-anemones on board for additional protection. Small fishes, known as clown

When they touch the tentacles of a sea-anemone most fish are caught, stung and eaten. But there are some, such as this yellow-tailed anemone fish hiding amongst the tentacles of a green bubble anemone, that are immune from attack and are protected by the anemone's formidable battery of stinging cells. They seem not to be immune at first, but approach and touch the anemone several times as if building up resistance. It is thought that the fish slowly covers itself with mucus from the anemone, which provides it with a protective coat.

fishes, actually live amongst the tentacles of sea-anemones without coming to harm. And the young of cod and other sea fishes sometimes seek refuge in the tentacles of floating jellyfish and Portuguese men-of-war.

Hedgehogs and spiny ant-eaters curl into a ball, the spiny back protecting the more vulnerable belly. Pangolins have thick, body scales and armadillos have a tough, outer hide, and they too roll up when danger threatens. On a smaller scale, the pill bug (one of the woodlice) and the pill millipede roll themselves up into complete armour-plated spheres, their hinged exoskeletons protecting their entire body.

Spines are a useful last resort. Puffer fish blow themselves up like spiny balloons preventing any predatory fish from biting them. Sticklebacks are swallowed by voracious pikes, only to be spat out again. The spines of the dorsal fin stick into the roof of the predator's mouth and the discomfort causes it to spit out the tiny fish. Horned sharks have just two spines. The leading edge of each dorsal fin is a spine, and they are sufficient to make an angel shark cough up its meal and allow the smaller shark to live another day.

◄

(Opposite page) The spiny pufferfish not only has a skin covered in spines for protection, but it can also blow itself up like a football, making it very difficult for a predator to take a bite.

◄

Fan-worms live in tubes. When feeding they have a crown of feather-like tentacles that filter food particles from the water, but if the pigment eyespots on the filaments detect the shadow of a passing fish, the worms pull down into their tubes in an instant.

▼

The white-spined lion fish advertises that its spines are capable of delivering a deadly venom with a display of very bright warning colours.

The caterpillars of many moths and butterflies protect themselves using colour. Those with poisons and poisonous spines have bright colours. There are those that mimic other dangerous creatures such as snakes, and there are others, such as the larvae of swallowtail butterflies, that mimic everyday things like bird droppings and, therefore, go unseen.

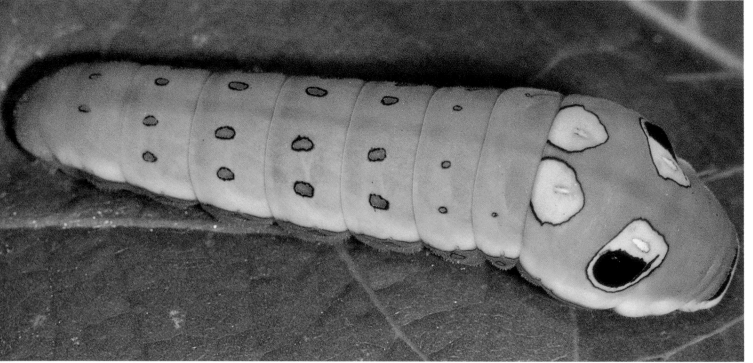

Adult butterflies, like their caterpillar stages, show mimicry too. The owl butterflies of Costa Rica have large eyespots on the hind wings and when the wings are open the effect is that of an owl's face. The butterfly's body and antenna even look like the owl's beak.

Peacock butterflies have small eyespots along the outside of the wings. This misdirects pecking beaks to the wing edge and away from the body.

The willow grouse has 2 anti-predator mechanisms. It blends in with its background and shuts down its body. During the short Arctic summer, its plumage consists mainly of various shades of brown with which it is well-camouflaged in the browns and greens of spring, summer and autumn. But in the winter, it has white feathers all over with which it blends in with its snowy environment. If a predator is close by, it can virtually shut down its heart and reduce breathing to a mere tickover. If detected, it can start up instantly and escape.

The bush thick-knee or stone curlew has a clever distraction display to entice predators away from its nest. It feigns a broken wing and the predator, anticipating an easy meal, follows it. At the last moment the bird flees and its nest is safe.

(Opposite page) Frogs and toads tend to be vulnerable to attack from birds, snakes and mammals, but many have colourful displays that either deter or startle. Arrow poison frogs from South and Central America are some of the most poisonous animals known to man and their bright colours tell other animals to stay clear. The poison is in the skin, and local tribesmen use it to tip their arrows and spears.

The oriental fire-bellied toad has a trick up its sleeve ... or on its belly. When threatened, it throws itself upside down and exposes the bright red-and-black colours on its underside. The effect is to startle and frighten away the predator. If the attacker is unimpressed, the toad is a dead one.

INDEX

ACKNOWLEDGEMENTS

BRUCE COLEMAN Jen & Des Bartlett, 41, 156, 162 • Erwin & Peggy Bauer, 36 bottom • Nigel Blake, title page bottom, 183 • Jane Burton, 96 top, 119, 162-3, 173 • B & C Calhoun, 174 • Gerald Cubitt, 15 right • Peter Davey, 52-3 • A J Deane, 147 bottom • Francisco Erize, 132-3, 166-7 • John Fennell, 133 bottom • M P L Fogden 146 top, 172 right • Jeff Foott, 55 bottom, 59, 100 • Michael Freeman, 54 top, 101 • C B Frith, 42 • Dennis Green, 139, 168 • Pekka Helo, 149 top • Carol Hughes, 87, 180-1 • John Kenfield, 54 bottom • Wayne Lankinen, 85 • Werner Layer, 159 • George McCarthy, 172 left • Norman Myers, 122 • Graham Pizzey, 43 • Dieter & Mary Plage, 7, 19 top • Goetz D Plage, 108 right • Fritz Prenzel, 97 • Hans Reinhard, 86, 141, 148, 152, 165 bottom, 187, back jacket top left • Carl Roessler, 129 • Alan Root, 78 • John Shaw, 175 right • Kim Taylor, 107• Norman Tomalin, 71 bottom, 160 • John Visser, 150, 152 • Carl Wallace, 175 left • Uwe Walz, 111 bottom • Peter Ward, 65 • Barrie Wilkins, 170 • Rod Williams, 27 • Bill Wood, 128-9 Worldwide Fund for Nature - G W Frame, 34 top left • Konrad Wothe, 53• Gunter Ziesler, 6, 9 left, 14 top, 14 bottom, 23, 34 top right, 108 left, 155, 163 • J Zwanenpoel, 15 left NATURAL HISTORY PHOTOGRAPHIC AGENCY Anthony Bannister, 11, 121, 131, 133 top, 153 • G I Bernard, 77, 146 bottom, 171, 181 bottom • Stephen Dalton, 75 bottom, 92, 93 left, 93 right, 94, 95 left, 106, 110 top, 111 top, 142 • Nigel Dennis, contents page, 52 • Peter Johnson, 16 bottom, 39 top, 47, 51 • Stephen Krasemann, half-title top, 18 top, 181 top, 184 bottom • Gérard Lacz, front jacket, 40, 58 • Michael Leach, 76 top • Eero Murtomäki, 136, 149 bottom • Tsuneo Nakamura, 178 • Haroldo Palo, 166 right • P D Pickford, 22 • John Shaw, 109 top, 125, 134-5, 184 top, back jacket top right • Silvestris, 83 • Martin Wendler, 150-1 • Bill Wood, 73 top, 126-7 NATURAL HISTORY PHOTOGRAPHIC AGENCY - ANT 103 • Kelvin Aitken, 91 • Barbara Todd, 33 • R J Tomkins, 32 • Cyril Webster, 75 top • D Whitford, 185 NATURE PHOTOGRAPHERS S C Bisserôt, 88, 186 • Peter Craig-Cooper, 16 top • M Gore, 21 • James Hancock, 116 left • Ed Lemon, 10 • Hugh Miles, 18 bottom, 35 top • Don Smith, 166 left • Paul Sterry, 28 • Roger Tidman, 82 • Hugo van Lawick, 24, 25 left, 50, 50-1 OXFORD SCIENTIFIC FILMS 61 right • Doug Allan, 44 • Anthony Bannister, 71 top • Rafi Ben Shahar, 35 bottom, 61 left • G I Bernard, 105, 113 • Eciton Burchelli, 145 • Densey Cline, 66 • Judd Cooney, 60 • Sarah Cunliffe, 179 top • Stephen Dalton, 165 top • Phil Devries, 169 • Stephen Downer, back jacket bottom • Frederik Ehrenstron, 112,   127 • Michael Fogden, 182 • David C Fritts, 72 • Max Gibbs, 177, 179 bottom • Laurence Gould, 128 • David Macdonald, 38, 39 bottom • Mantis Wildlife Films, 74 • Roland Mayr, 130, 144 • Godfrey Merlen, 110 bottom, 164 • Colin Milkins, 120 • Owen Newman, 9 right • Stan Osolinski, 19 bottom 98, 99, 109 bottom, 137 • Richard Packwood, 49 top, 78-9 • K Porter,'130-1 • David Shale, 114, 117, 126 • Philip Sharpe, 147 top • Steve Turner, 34 bottom • Tom Ulrich, half-title bottom, 25 right, 124 • Kim Westerskov, 167 • Claudia Wight - Partridge Productions, 17 bottom • Norbert Wu, 57 OXFORD SCIENTIFIC FILMS - ANIMALS ANIMALS John Chellman, 20, 37 • Michael Dick, 17   top • Breck C Kent, title page top, 63, 76 bottom, 132 • Richard Kolar, 180 • Zig Leszczynski, 73 bottom, 96 bottom • Patti Murray, 81 • Alan G Nelson, 56, 70 • J H Robinson, 69 • Carl Roessler, 13 OXFORD SCIENTIFIC FILMS - OKAPIA Jeff Foott, 31 PLANET EARTH K & K Ammann, 68 • Philip Chapman, 123 • Peter David, 64 • John Lythgoe, 79 • Duncan Morrell, 32-3, 55 top • Christian Petron, 80 • Mike Potts, 84 • Jonathan Scott, 12, 48, 49 bottom • Marty Snyderman, 90 top, 90 bottom • Gilbert van Ryckevorsel, 36 top PREMAPHOTOS WILDLIFE K G Preston-Mafham, 95 right